Breaking Cover – 1

An Anthology of Country Tales

by **Jackie Drakeford**

Published in 2013 by Skycat Publications
Vaiseys Farm, Brent Eleigh, Suffolk CO10 9 PA
Email info@skycatpublications.com
www.skycatpublications.com

ISBN 978-0-9567029-6-8

Printed by Lavenham Press
Arbons House, 47 Water Street, Lavenham, Suffolk CO10 9RN
Telephone: +44 (0)1787 247436
Email: enquiries@lavenhamgroup.co.uk

Acknowledgements

Some of the articles in this collection are previously unpublished, while versions of the others have previously appeared in *Shooting Times, Countryman's Weekly* or *Sporting Shooter*, for which thanks are extended to the editors involved.

Photographs remain copyright of the author, except where otherwise indicated. Thanks are due to F. Sechiari for allowing the use of her photographs, and to Janet George of the Indigo Stud, Kidderminster, for the photographs of her Irish Draught horses on pages 50-56, which are not the horses described in the accompanying text. Guest articles on page 117 and 125 are copyright of Phillip Blackman.

Other titles by the same author

Breaking Cover - 2
published 2013

The Working Lurcher - The Traditional Skills
published 2006

The House Lurcher
first published 2003, second edition 2010

Rabbit Control
first published 2002, revised edition 2008

Understanding the Working Lurcher
published 2000

Working Ferrets
published 1996, second edition 2011

Essential Care in the Field
Co-authored with Mark Elliott M.R.C.V.S
First published 2007
revised 2013 by Skycat publications

Essential Care for Dogs
Published 2005

About the author

The author is well-known for her books and articles on country sports and working dogs, which appear regularly in a variety of fieldsports publications. Now living in rural Sussex, she grew up in the New Forest, where the Game Laws have been a thorn in the flesh of the locals ever since William the Conqueror came over and started acting as if he owned the place. Horses, hounds, lurchers, terriers and ferrets have figured largely in her life from an early age, and she has a deep respect and appreciation of the wild creatures that pepper her tales.

Jackie is a Kennel Club Accredited Instructor and dog behaviour trainer, working with an integrated veterinary practice as well as writing articles and lecturing on dog behaviour.

Contents

Back seat driver ...

... says it all really!!

Introduction

Those of us who pursue countryside activities know that they are the greatest of levellers: one minute birdsong, next minute cowpat. Here we have a collection of wry snippets about those situations that can arise when keeping hunting dogs, going out in the beating line or following the hunt. We accompany the author through mud, nettles, brambles, hell and high water, waiting for recalcitrant dogs or attempting smooth talking when straight talking would be more natural.

We meet a variety of country characters with unexpected skills and endless patience, who mostly remain good-humoured despite encountering extreme discomfort, or being caught in circumstances for which a rustic background gives little preparation.

We also meet as guest writer the author's long-suffering partner, who has to dig the deepest holes and net the worst buries, and who provides his own insider information on what really happens out shooting.

Padding through the text are the real stars of each tale: the silent lurchers with their glowing eyes and high standards that their humans seldom manage to meet, the feisty terriers that give road to nothing and nobody, the horses that could never be described as steady, the sinewy ferrets that creep underground into darkness. Anyone who has had anything to do with any of these creatures in their preferred environment will recognise the voice of authenticity on every page.

Some of these tales have been previously published in a variety of countryside magazines, and others are in print for the first time. Many were written before the restrictions caused by the Hunting Act, and describe incidents which were legal at the time they took place. They will strike chords of happy memories with readers who remember those times, and provide a sound reference for those whose hunting days have come later.

One

Small Biting Things

IALWAYS thought I would hate working with a dog that "opened up" (made a noise) but when it came to it, I wasn't bothered at all. One of the many things I like about lurchers is their silence, something I regularly remind The Colly of as she indulges in her We're Going Ferreting song-and-dance routine on seeing the nets being packed. But she is quiet when it matters, unlike my friend Harris the Hawk's little whirrier (whippet/terrier cross) which sings like a canary. H gets his nickname from being tall, thin and hook-nosed with the prey-drive of a Tyrannosaurus; the whirrier is small, driven and psychopathic. They make a good team.

We first went ferreting together some years ago, when he had a totally novice team of ferrets, some of which had never left home before, and Scruffs, the whirrier, had only been out a couple of times at the fag-end of the previous season. It was just after harvest, and we were raring to get started again. To maintain the interest of his volatile little dog, H said we wouldn't net the first bury but let the rabbits bolt free. You have to admire the tenacity of this type of lurcher, for she gave each rabbit a good workout, and was very unlucky not to catch. Some lurcher types would have become discouraged, but not Scruffs. Most of the ferrets got the hang of the job

Credit: Fay Sechiari

quickly, but one was scared of the dark and the possibility of there being Goblins down there, so instead she found a soft spot to rest against my chest upholstery, where she seemed perfectly at ease. There was a good view from up there as well.

Having established the principles, we thought we'd better catch some rabbits, so the next bury was netted and worked as normal. The great thing about purse nets is that the dog gets the feel of catching rabbits, though Scruffs lost it a bit with the first one, which was carried on several victory laps around the bury while still in the net. After that, she settled down and worked steadily, while the nervous ferret was extracted from my cleavage and returned to the ferret box. A pile of rabbits later, H went on to the next bury while I stayed behind picking up nets. Just as I finished, I heard Scruffs yipping, and thought, "Oh good, there'll be one there then", sauntering over to the bury in no particular hurry. But as I topped the rise above it, I saw H sitting down, and wondered if he'd hurt himself. Further perusal showed that he was sitting on a deer, and neither of them was best pleased about it. As he couldn't reach his lead, he needed me to remove his dog from the scene so he could let Mrs. Deer go without an action replay of the previous couple of minutes, which had proved a nineteen inch dog can drop a roe with little effort; luckily H had got to the beast before any damage was done. I took Scruffs out of sight and yes she was very annoyed, the release was accomplished, and then H explained to me that he had been sitting there wishing I'd hurry up, while watching a seething infestation of lice and ticks crawling across or attached to the deer's hide beneath him. About then we each started to itch.

We ferreted three more buries, by which time we were scratching like gibbons. We shuffled and chafed our way back, picking off lice and spreading others around in our eyebrows, our ears, and other places best not discussed in public. We thanked the landowner (while trying not to scratch too obviously in front of him) and left his usual two brace of rabbits; he said not to worry about the deer, he was sure it would be fine and anyway his ancient retired greyhound was always doing that. We didn't ask about the lice: maybe they

just slid off a greyhound's shiny coat and broke their legs. We wriggled and scratched constantly on the drive back to H's, and then I scratched on my own all the way home, wondering how to fumigate a car. On arrival, I pushed past the dogs and the Sahib, saying I had to have a bath right now, and when I'd had it I'd tell him why.

It was years ago, and I'm scratching as I'm writing this.

Two

Bobbery Packery

HUNTING with a bobbery pack is seriously good fun or else the stuff of which nightmares are made. If you want to be even nominally in charge, each dog should be trained and worked solo before it is ever unleashed as part of a group, otherwise you are in the red-faced realms of: 'one dog is a dog, two dogs is 'alf a dog, and three dogs is no dogs at all' helplessly watching a line of disappearing backsides heading for somewhere you aren't welcome.

The contents can vary, but you will need at least one cover-basher, a sprinter, and a nose dog; one retriever is handy, and if working your own land you can indulge in something that makes houndly music. In areas where others have access, discretion is best, even though you have full permission and the landowner's blessing, because for some reason certain people can get entirely the wrong idea.

Worked as a group, dogs naturally divide, as the late Brian Plummer observed, into 'find' dogs and 'catch' dogs. If a key member of one discipline is absent, then another will change roles to cover the gap, and when the pack re-assembles on a different day with the original dog present, the other will revert to its preferred task. A bobbery pack is the ultimate democracy: each dog knows what it is best at, and no dog tells

it to do something else. I borrowed a corgi one day when I was short of bush-bashers, and he proved a natural; unfortunately he then went home and did for the pet guinea pig, so I wasn't allowed to use him again.

Not every dog is suitable. I have been out with a collie that ran itself inside out trying to round the rest of us up; being hopelessly outpaced by the lurchers it didn't achieve much except for dicing with death when it tried to herd the terriers instead. Terriers are very much not herdable. Bird dogs may be brilliant at ranging the moors finding coveys, but for ground game on small lowland farms their methods are hopeless: I have had a hard-bitten pack of five lurchers slinking to heel in silent fury as a Weimaraner rocking-horsed its way round a hundred-and-some acres, pushing all the game either to ground or across the boundary. You do need dogs dedicated to finding and catching, by whatever means are best for each quarry, and they need to be team players. Seven dogs running in seven different directions will only make you wish you'd gone fishing.

I have twice had a sheep on the team. They have limited uses as hunting companions but are wonderful for keeping dogs stock-steady. Each had been hand-reared and liked dogs, and would come bounding across to join in as soon as it saw us. Sheep don't like foxes; these were good 'marking' sheep, and would stare and stamp if there was one hidden in the brambles. You haven't seen comedy until you've seen a fox attempting to dodge a team of dogs by trying to hide under a sheep that wants to butt it. Never give a sheep a biscuit though, or it will try to come home with you.

The pure joy of bobbery packery is watching dogs working as dogs were designed to work, the action ebbing and flowing, the sudden yip-yip-yip of a terrier close behind something in cover as the running dogs get up on their toes and place themselves where instinct and practice tell them quarry is likely to break. Every scientist studying dog behaviour should be made to watch dogs hunting in packs before they put pen to paper - we'd read a lot less nonsense. Though a familiar team will work like oiled machinery, you can also - I've seen it done - assemble a random group of mutts who have never met before, and within minutes they will have melded into a useful unit. Like Army training, as long as the drill has been installed (in this case basic obedience) you can slot any group into any group and get results, but the crack teams work best together because they know each other to the inch.

We had an independent moo of a Lakeland terrier who had to be watched or she would skulk off on a project of her own, and as she became old, deaf and doddery, she developed a tendency to run the 'heel' line. One day, we mislaid her while working up a deep drainage ditch, and I drew the short straw. No point calling as she couldn't hear us, and was pretty selective when she could, so I started back to look for her.

For once, she wasn't being awkward at all, but using her considerable scenting skills had tracked back two hundred yards to pick up a rabbit, and was driving it at a fast scurry all the way forwards up the ditch towards the others. My apologies to her were as fulsome as my curses had been dark and bitter; being a Lakeland, she didn't care either way.

Well before tiresome laws that now restrict our hunting to rats and rabbits, I remember working out a line of overgrown blackthorn and bramble with the usual suspects, nice and steady but clearly onto something. This day it was the psychopathic Patterdale that hitched up her skirts and started threading up-tempo through the thicket; the Sahib waved his cap and the Bedlington Thing, still a spotty youth, bunched and ran, his dam tearing up the far side of the ditch in parallel, in case we had a bolt that way. There was a whooshing, crackling and splashing, a 'thwack' that was to become his trademark, and then my cute fluffy Bedlington lurcher came galloping back to me wearing a very annoyed fox like a giant moustache. It was his first, and the only one he ever retrieved alive; he had a lucky grip which meant it couldn't damage him, and he was thrilled with himself. His old Granny Worm, too slow for running by then, pushed her sleeves back and leaned over. "This is what you do with these, my boy" she said, finishing the problem with one decisive bite. That's teamwork.

Three

Down on the Farm

FOR years I had a part-time job on a mixed arable and free-range poultry farm. The poultry brought in a steady stream of foxes, and the crops were attractive to rabbits and deer; the work was hard but the perks were immense. It was for there that I developed my preferred type of lurcher, that could find and despatch its quarry in the same field, because it was all too easy for vermin to cross the farm boundaries. I also learned a lot about poultry, as everything was kept the old-fashioned way.

Three flocks of laying chickens were the mainstay, comprising the steady layers, the old 'ladies' that laid the bigger eggs that were so popular with customers, and pullets just coming on. We also had free-range ducks, including a handsome Aylesbury x Appleyard drake, forty-odd free-range Norfolk Bronze and black turkeys, including two stags, and a scattering of pretty mixed bantams, including two cockerels. Everything you ever heard about bantam cocks is true: these two would travel the length of the farm to beat each other up no matter how we tried to keep them apart; we would tenderly nurse one or the other back to health, and as soon as it was out again, it would be looking for the other feller to spill his beer and look at his bird. Eventually the fox solved

the problem, though I suspect the little cockerel sold his life dearly; the other one lasted quite a few years more before meeting the same fate.

The turkey hens reminded me of Olive Oyl in the 'Popeye' cartoons: they were leggy and dim but very sweet-natured, had huge eyelashes, and little cheeping voices quite at odds with their size. Turkey chicks are like tiny ostriches to look at, but they can fly almost from the shell. They are engaging creatures, very curious and friendly. Turkey eggs were another perk of the job, but the laying season is short so we had only a few weeks to enjoy those fat cream-coloured brown-freckled eggs. Large and almost pyramidal in shape, they were impossible to fit in an eggcup but just the job with a thick rasher of bacon once the early chores were completed.

The turkey stags - one bronze, one black - could not be let out together, so one would have the morning shift and the other the afternoon. One day, the farmhand got drunk (a regular happening) and let both out together: I promise you, you haven't lived until you've broken up a fight between two twenty-pound turkeys while being 'helped' by an inebriated old rustic who kept swaying underfoot and intoning "Oh naw, yew caahn't stop 'em fighting once they start". Well you can and I did, but it wasn't easy: man, do they have some spurs on them.

Ducks are comedians when alive, delicious when roasted, and lay ambrosial eggs. They bring foxes in like nothing else, stray all over the place and my, do they take some keeping clean: they'd create mud in a desert and their muck stinks appallingly. They were never in a hurry to go to bed at night, unlike the chooks which packed themselves tidily off to roost as the sun went down. You had to round up the ducks quite fiercely, and there would always be one blighter that wouldn't go in. Nevertheless, I'm fond of ducks, and enjoyed having them about, despite the hassle.

Now, country living can be a hotbed of deviant sex in any case, but you never saw anything as complicated as that which went on with mixed free-range. The stroppy turkey stag had been hatched under a hen, so he was carnally fixated on the laying stock. A twenty-pound turkey trying to tread a three-pound hen can only end in a feathery mat, and meanwhile the tall anxious turkey hens went unsatisfied until the friendly stag was released in his turn. Turkeys have problems mating naturally anyway, but at least he got the courting right and cheered them up. That was apart from the one turkey hen with which the bantam cock was obsessed. He would woo her with his crooning, then when he judged she had been flattered into compliance, he would leap onto her broad back and almost disappear at the rump end with a great deal of fluttering. Presently his passion would urge him to peck the

back of her head, which meant running the length of her, up her ostrich neck, a brief grip of her head feathers and then he would lose his balance and fall off. From there, he would rouse his feathers as if he'd meant to do that all along, and resume his serenading from the ground until he judged that she was feeling receptive again. It kept both of them occupied for hours.

Then there was the drake. He had been hatched under a hen as well, so he would court the laying hens, and while his consummations were not fatal in the way the turkey stag's were, it was clear that he did not really hit the spot, especially when he was trying to lure the hens into water first. They just did not understand, and no matter how he preened and posed, remained resolutely on dry land. There was a similar level of stress when hens hatched out ducklings, which ran to the shallow water-containers provided for them and set sail, leaving an anxious hen hopping from foot to foot on dry land, calling them plaintively.

When regulations changed, making it difficult to sell free-range fresh-killed birds at the farm gate, we packed in the turkeys, though they provided my Christmas money for several years. We kept a couple of old turkey hens and the nice-natured stag just for a bit of colour around the place, along with a brace of wonky old ducks. Eventually the fox did for the lot in one night; we took a suitable revenge in turn. After that, we just kept chickens until the farmer sold up and retired. I missed the farm: I'd had a lot of fun there and brought on several generations of dogs hunting a broad spectrum of quarry too.

Four

Black Death's Debut

IWAS lucky in that all my puppy owners have kept in touch, and I had been hearing good reports on their progress. Mine had occupied her puppyhood with nothing more demanding than a little training and a lot of bushing: "less is more" with my line of lurchers, and you need a very light touch with them. Temperamentally, she was very puppyish still, with much deerhound in her, and I had looked at her with lamping or ferreting in mind and thought that no, she is not ready yet. Then not long ago, I looked and thought: Yes it's time.

Bushing teaches a pup a lot about using her nose, crossing difficult terrain, chasing and striking, and the most important thing of all in my eyes, which is coming back. At a year old, the Black Death had caught a decent tally of rabbits, and a few rats of varying kinds, showing herself to be committed and talented. She had finished her first season at eleven months old, and come back from it quickly. We were having a little teenage independence here and there, but if this was as bad as it got I wouldn't be complaining. BD had been a charming pup, but she still had a lot of developing to do, mentally and physically. I had laid the best foundations that I could; now we would see what we had to build upon.

Some wild weather and a kind friend combined to offer the perfect start to her lamping. Changes in land ownership or farming management had seen much of my lamping permission either gone or unsuitable for a learner. Mostly a pup is a complete pillock for the first few runs, and if the idiocy includes running wild and putting every rabbit to ground, or making a noise, or disappearing into the night, or any one of several more common but irritating sins, that piece of ground has been spoiled for lamping for some time, so it is a really generous gesture for someone to share their permission to bring on a tyro pup. We stalked out into the wild weather, and I felt that strange combination of deep peace and predator's concentration that settles on me once out in the darkness.

The first slip belonged to my host, and his pup, the same age but far more mature and experienced than mine, ran down true to the beam, closed the gap on her rabbit and worked it like a seasoned dog, flicking it out of the hedge and back into the open before catching it almost at his feet. Very nice. I swung the light around to find most of the other rabbits had run in and the obliging sitter I had seen seconds ago was sitting no more, but then found another suitable candidate, sighted the pup and started walking her forward. Like many a pup before her, she disappeared after a different rabbit, and I switched off the beam to await her return. Over by the hedge, I could see a glow of light where my friend was standing with his dogs, and then something large, soft and warm enveloped the back of my neck, and the world stopped.

You will be pleased to know that I neither made a noise nor had a childish accident. For a moment I didn't even breathe. When I did, I became aware of a vast horse nuzzling me in a friendly manner, wondering what I was doing in its field. At about the same time, the puppy returned, so I bid the horse goodbye and walked on trembling legs to the field boundary and my fellow hunters. We hadn't expected horses in that field.

Lamping by turns, we crossed another couple of fields, which gave the pup two more slips, neither of which impressed, and my colleague's other dog took a rabbit after a very long slip and a superb run. There was one more field to try. Our attempts to be quiet were marred by deep squelching mud in the gateway, and then to add to the serenity of the night, I stumbled by accident through several patches of dry weeds that were nearly as tall as I was. Finally, the gods of lamping smiled on me, and I saw a rabbit on the far side of a large weed. I sighted the pup and started to walk forward: the rabbit was sitting up and flicking its ears so she actually saw it, and everything fell into place. Starting at a hesitant trot, she closed on it, and then the rabbit ran and so did she. The pup ran to block it from cover, those bushing lessons working well, struck, missed and somersaulted. The rabbit turned for home but the pup was already up and running. At her next strike, the rabbit leaped clean over the top of her, twisting belly-up in the air, landed and ran two strides, and the Black Death put in a mighty wrench and picked it up. She lay down with the rabbit pinned between her front paws, utterly spent mentally and physically. Only a fool would have pressed her for a retrieve now; there would be plenty of retrieves later as she grew more confident. I walked the few paces towards her, put a hand on the rabbit, which was unharmed and very put out, and made a great fuss of her before gently taking it. She

followed back across the field, with me carrying what would always be the best rabbit of her entire life. We had achieved what we had come out for, and it was time to stop.

My friend is a Northerner, and understands the priorities of life.

"Tea?" he said.

Five

Freestyle Ferreting

WE were ferreting a large private garden on a property that had recently changed owners. The new people had installed rabbit fencing, but the contractors had fenced through several rabbit buries, so the rabbits were still passing through with only minor inconvenience. Within the garden, in deep sandy soil, was a chain of very big well-established buries set under shrubs, log piles and small trees, and there were the obligatory caches of broken glass and pottery, with side dishes of rusting metal and half-hearted coils of wire, that you often find in the hinterland of properties like this. It wasn't a place that was safe for a dog, partly due to the trappy shrubbery and hazardous rubbish, but mostly because of the unfenced side by the narrow country lane being used as a rat-run by motorists in the know, and the stout electric fence keeping the cattle in on the other side.

Ferreting without a dog is something I do purely because it might lead to other, better permission (it often does) but it isn't normally anything like as much fun. However, I was about to experience a whole new dimension in dogless ferreting.

Buck and I netted up every hole we could find, which took an hour and a half and probably two hundred nets. Because of my old age and infirmity, the system is that he does all the difficult places and I do the easy ones, so while he was crawling under spiky shrubs and risking tetanus from the debris on the ground, I was netting the open holes and occasionally disappearing knee deep with a startled comment as the soil collapsed into these pock-marked buries. Without a dog to mark the buries, we felt disadvantaged: there was some rabbit sign about, but nothing to justify the numbers the owners said they had seen - but then we all know how many rabbits look like a hundred to a landowner! Next to the garden was the orchard, and the buries in there looked much livelier, so while Buck was still occupied with the difficulties of the garden, I netted a further five buries in the open, though of course there was a small pile of broken fencing, concrete slabs and wire left exactly on top of the biggest and most promising bury.

Back in the garden, we took up position and down went the ferrets. Now Buck is one of these ridiculously athletic people who runs half-marathons for fun, so what followed was like ferreting with Roadrunner. There would be a blur going one way almost meeting a blur going the other, the second one wearing a big grin and waving a rabbit. Sometimes the blur would vault across the electric fence, with an appropriate remark if he caught the current, or leap Nureyev-like from fence-post to fence-post to dive between some fascinated cattle and collect a ferret. While our technical merit was without blemish (we only lost one rabbit all day, and that was out of the cow field) the artistic interpretation delivered a totally new experience. Much as I enjoy ferreting with the Sahib, you don't get this level of pole-dancing, not to mention the high-speed retrieves.

We moved steadily across the garden, working bury after bury, most of which, due to the time of year, only had a pair or two pairs of rabbits in. Having cleared the garden of the dozen or so rabbits that were in there, we approached the orchard with that holiday feeling of having completed the hard work and being about to have some fun. We could not net across the boundary, although I had permission from the neighbouring landowner, because of the cattle. Luckily

Credit: Fay Sechiari

someone came to feed them just when they could not have been more of a nuisance to us, and they set off across to the other side of their field.

The orchard rabbits were big and bolted well, Buck chasing one pop-hole escapee down the field and putting so much pressure on it that it panicked and backnetted two buries down, one of the reasons that we net all the buries before we start. "Who needs a lurcher?" he said, as he deftly extracted it. Then he really excelled himself, when I was looking up at a light aircraft instead of down at the nets, and a rabbit bolted on my side, kicked out of the net and shot under the electric fence. Uttering a well-known phrase, he bounded through the fence and launched after the rabbit in a mighty leap - and landed with his feet on its back legs as it was running! "You should see me hare-coursing" he said.

We finished the orchard and the day with a pile of beautiful quality rabbits, and as we had an order from the butcher, we went straight there to drop them off. I would estimate a good third of the catch had been backnetted because we weren't able to net the cattle field side of the boundary, and the day had gone far better than either of us had anticipated. Despite the lack of a lurcher, we'd had great fun, and on the way home I was pondering on how we could get freestyle ferreting added to the Olympic Games.

Six

The Colly

MANY Christmases ago, the Colly came home to stay. The Sahib insists I never actually mentioned it to him. He was vaguely aware of a small brown scampering thing, but then we have all sizes of brown things living here, many of which scamper, and one more is neither here nor there.

The other dogs noticed: the terrier developed that green-eyed glow that indicates she is hearing The Voices that tell her to kill small weak creatures and even, come to that, big strong creatures. I had to watch the terrier. The Bedlington Thing insisted he'd never seen her before in his life, never met her mother, and there had to be some mistake. The old silver dog regally ignored her, and the fawn bitch, her grandmother, gathered her in, washed, entertained and generally fostered her. I fear she may also have told her many tales of predation on a variety of quarry, and she certainly had those tales to tell. The hens noticed an animal that was small enough to peck; I had to watch the hens as much as the terrier, for they go for eyes, and it isn't a good start.

I had visited the Colly every week at the breeder's, so we knew each other by the time she moved in, and she knew her name as well. Once they have their paws under the table, other names suggest themselves: I should have called her Feral. For

the first year of her life, she would not eat out of a bowl, but had to have her food on the ground, whereupon she would stalk, pounce and shake the living daylights out of it. Wiping blood and bits of green tripe off the walls became a regular task, and we don't get that many visitors anyway. Then she would carry off her newly-killed lunch to a safe place to eat it: under the dresser was good until she grew too big. Glowing eyes and loud chomping created a domestic background that wasn't exactly relaxing. Often the safe place was me, and I had to sit quietly with a small jackal on my lap, trying to ignore grisly gnawing and soft growls as she intimidated her food from any thoughts it might have had about coming back to life. There was no making her eat normally: any interference and she would not eat at all. Those who think a puppy will not starve itself should try a lurcher sometime - or maybe not. Thank goodness for washing machines, say I.

Her favourite place to sleep was across my shoulders with her face down my cleavage, and you can keep those remarks to yourself. If I was busy, the fawn bitch would take over as babysitter; in extreme cases and with an expression of deep suffering, her father would tolerate her snuggling up, and probably ordered her not to fidget. The dogs taught her manners in a way I never could, and every week or so she went back to her breeder to play with her siblings, coming back as rude and defiant as any child that has been to an indulgent relative for the day.

A very good lurcherwoman once said to me: "They are wonderful puppies. They are wonderful adults. But they are horrible adolescents". She was so right. It is no accident that so many dogs seen in rescue are adolescents. But if we can only weather the storm, at the other side of the 'Kevins' is the lurcher you wanted all along. The Colly was an exception: she was an amazingly 'different' puppy, and I don't recollect her having an adolescence at all. She went through a phase where she bit like a fiend, not puppy mouthing but sinking her needles in and latching on. She came out of that and developed a habit of jumping onto tables and window-sills, and I caught her standing in the sink several times. She was shy and fey and tricky. She grew out of all of it. She's a cracking lurcher. So will yours be, whatever it is like now. We forget, between puppies, just what challenging little beggars they are. Hang on in there: normality is just around the corner.

Seven

Darwin Awards

THE Darwin Awards subsection 'rodents' held their finals in the South this year. The first we were aware was when we were both awoken by a horrible screaming noise in the back garden. Intellectually, one is not always at one's best at moments like this, so I shoved the Sahib out of bed to go and investigate. He found that a rat had gnawed its way into the ferretry, and its mortal remains lay by the rat hole, through which three ferrets had already escaped. There was also a terrier with a bitten nose, and an extremely pungent smell in the back porch. In the darkness, the Sahib blocked the escape hole, set every live trap we possessed, left all the ferret carrying boxes open, left the shed door open, and came back to bed. We were up well before dawn, not having been able to sleep much because we were so worried about the missing ferrets.

Nothing was waiting for us in the traps or boxes, but down by the shed, a ferret kitten crept out at the sound of my voice. She was covered in filth, had sustained a few rat-bites, and was understandably very excited: "You should just see what's under here".

Having realised that it was my voice she'd responded to, I spoke some more, and from under the shed slithered the

second ferret kit, similarly puffed up, and similarly bitten. That left only one missing, which under the Law of Sod was not mine, but had been lent to me by a good friend who did want her back in the summer for breeding. Further adding to my cheer was the free-range mixed poultry in the yard over the back from us; although we frequently helped out when marauding foxes called, it was not going to enhance neighbourly relations if a ferret killed everything off instead. I summoned the lurchers and we searched everywhere to see if we could find the ferret before the poultry was let out, but found nothing.

At the end of what seemed to be a very long day, there was still no sign of the third ferret. I was in the back porch telling the ancient terrier to get a move on when, it was my voice again, I saw a small triangular face peeping from under the pallets on which the dog beds stood. She wanted to come to me but was very frightened, and after twenty minutes or so of coming half out and darting back again, she finally allowed me to extract her with the aid of a frozen squirrel - obviously most of us have a few of those to hand for this kind of emergency.

Her musk glands were empty (and I knew just where they had been emptied!) and she was exhausted, almost in a state of collapse. Luckily, ferrets are resilient creatures, and after a good meal and a sleep, she appeared to be back to normal.

The terrier healed up without problems either, though I shall never know if it was the ferret or another rat that had bitten her. We put some special food down for the rats, and

some traps too, as well as upgrading the emergency repair on the ferret court, and having got everyone back safely, I relayed news of the drama to the sandy jill's owner. It really must have been Darwin night, because he told me that a rat had gnawed its way into his ferretry and paid the ultimate price as well. He was still rounding up some of his ferrets, and they were returning with evidence of having had conversations with rats too. He was very lucky to get one of them back, as the people who had found it, who knew nothing about ferrets, thought they would keep it as a pet. Can you imagine finding someone else's animal and just deciding to keep it? Fortunately the ferret nipped them, and so they changed their minds. Can you imagine letting a ferret you have only just found run around on your shoulders? There might have been a Darwin award for that as well.

So both of us now had our ferrets entered to rat, which wasn't in the master plan, but we can go with the flow if we have to.

Sharing this news with a friend of mine, he told me that he thought he'd had rats in his loft from strange noises heard in the night. On going up to investigate the next morning, he found that a mouse had gnawed its way into a sealed tub of poison, and the strange noises were caused by a mouse stuck in the tub rolling around on the floor. I relayed the tale to the Sahib, and he had the answer at once: the rodents were all suffering from depression!

Eight

Lamping the Devil

IT all looks different at night in the beam of your lamp, doesn't it? Especially on a slow night, when you stalk the fields with your trusty lurcher, getting more and more discouraged when rabbits you creep up on ever so slowly turn out to be crouching lumps of earth, or else crouching lumps of earth that you weren't creeping up slowly on at all suddenly sprout ears and little white fluffy tails, and run in the very direction you didn't want them to. Sometimes lumps of earth sprout wings and float into the air like giant moths, and you wonder how that could have happened until you remember about little owls. Sometimes there is an embarrassing incident with a partridge. It isn't all plain sailing for us warriors of the moonless night, I can tell you.

There are animals that appear in the beam looking like nothing you have ever seen, until your intellect catches up with your primordial hunter instinct to give you a clue. Primordial hunters didn't generally lamp, though. Maybe that is why we can be all over the place with our wildlife identification when we add a bright light: we simply aren't designed for it. I'm sure some of you will have seen the creature that is the size of a hare but doesn't move like a hare, has a piggy roach to its back but isn't a baby wild boar, pootles about on skimpy legs like a hedgepig but is far too big and not at all spiky, then looks up with a 'put that light out' expression just as you recognise it as a muntjac. How many of you have come up close and personal to a dark mass of anti-matter that suddenly wheels about and trots away with a hatstand on its head, or else been brought up short and disbelieving by a moving arrangement of green lights several feet off the ground? Faeries partying? Ha ha, blow me down: those are the eyes of the rest of the herd. The damned things catch me out every time, even though I know they live there. Then there is that moment of highly-strung disbelief when you have a dog heading fast down the beam to a perfectly placed sitter, and out of the darkness ambles a badger, right between hunter and hunted. Badgers can run a great deal faster than you might think, and it can take enormous commitment to avoid going into the shaving brush business.

I admit I have not always been a good person, but have I ever told you about the time the Devil himself appeared in front of me when I was lamping? There he was, caught in the beam and straight out of Denis Wheatley, accompanied by a charnel-house reek of old sweaty meat and ammonia, like a grave opening. At times like this, there is an interesting biological response in the human: some systems shut down and others go into overdrive. That which is customarily loose tightens, and much more riskily, that which is designed to be tight goes slack. My companion uttered a startled caw, and I wondered if he had been turned into a crow, but I didn't dare turn round to look. I was rooted to the ground, slack-jawed and glaze-eyed, and never even realised I was holding my breath until the lurcher dug me sharply in the thigh, and I let out a long gasp. She was trying to tell me to stop lamping the blasted goat and get on with finding her something she was allowed to chase.

Nine

The Hunt Puppy Show

THE Hunt Puppy Show is a piece of Old England, and anyone who has the chance to attend one will feel as if they have gently stepped back in time, the way a village cricket match or summer fete can take you. Its origins came about to thank the puppy-walkers for their efforts, and keep them sweet for the future, for once hound packs became more public and less under ownership of private individuals with their own estates, so hound puppies could no longer be left with cottagers or tenant farmers (whether they wanted to 'walk' them or not), and volunteers were needed instead.

Hound puppies are put out 'at walk' for a significant part of the first year or so of their lives, so that they can have more freedom and socialising than they would get in hunt kennels. The best puppy-walkers send their puppies back knowing their names (and preferably returning when called by them) familiar with domestic livestock, horses, poultry and cats (we hope chasing none of these) having met as many different kinds and ages of human as possible and being afraid of none of them, and having been taken out and about everywhere anyone can take a hound puppy or two. The old ideal was for the pups to have complete freedom to roam, but this is impractical and unsafe nowadays except in a very few areas,

and marauding hounds, even very young ones, can cause a lot of friction with neighbours. Therefore puppy-walking is no longer only for those with large tracts of land, but has opened out to include anyone who is willing and able to put time and effort into rearing and socialising young hounds. It is a huge amount of work, and essential to the development of good hounds, so puppy-walkers are cherished. Their thanks and reward is the Puppy Show, where they see their erstwhile young hooligans paraded in competition with the rest of the 'young entry', and have the chance to win trophies and receive keepsakes which somehow compensates for the ruined laundry, trashed gardens, and all the other destruction that can occur with large exuberant young hounds. Some people walk puppies for decades, some families for generations, and take great pleasure in watching 'their' hounds hunting year after year. Hounds never forget their walkers either, and will often break ranks at the Meet to greet them, though once the pack moves off, the huntsman's word is law, and their hounds are all business again.

Times change, and nowadays the Puppy Show, while still strictly by invitation only, will include hunt members, subscribers, and paid-up members of the supporters' clubs. For several weeks prior to the great day, everything that doesn't move is painted, creosoted or whitewashed at least once, and everything that can move is either greased or told to move faster. Grass is mown and strimmed to billiard-table smoothness, and sometimes there are even flowerbeds and hanging baskets (we are not talking about the sudden demise of any kennel staff by the use of the latter term here). On the day, we guests are each provided with a card (often very smart) giving the names and breeding of the puppies being shown, and the names of their puppy-walkers. Often there is also a full list of hounds in kennels, their breeding, and year of entry. This is very much appreciated by hound-savvy people: it gives an air of continuity, shows the longevity of the working hound, and for those like myself who are very keen on bloodlines, gives important information on the ancestry of the pack. Dress code is a little more relaxed, but the occasion is still formal. Gentlemen wear blazer, slacks and tie (old school if relevant) with appropriate shoes (no brothel-

creepers, please) and panama hat, or else a lightweight suit and hat, though nowadays when we don't all have a suit for every occasion, any formal suit and tie is acceptable for most hunts, and a hat, while desirable, is no longer mandatory.

Ladies wear summer dresses or suits, and hattage can be more frivolous; some do not wear hats nowadays, but when I started going to puppy shows, hat and gloves were essential trimmings to one's outfit, and footwear had to enclose the toes - no sandals! More modern puppy show attendees have been known to sport sandals, albeit very pretty ones (no flip-flops yet) and even I leave my gloves at home these days. Years ago, children had to be dressed formally too, but nowadays it seems usual for many of them to attend in 'slobs' order' and behave less than impeccably too, which is rather a pity. It doesn't kill children to learn that they have to be smart on occasion, and also be quiet, and leave their blasted beeping electronic games at home. At one recent Puppy Show, one teenage attendee was so important that she could not keep off her mobile phone for the duration of the judging, nor did

she think to discreetly leave the show area while she burbled her trivia. Every old fogey in the immediate vicinity, myself included, glared at her in an Osbert Lancaster cartoon sort of way, which eventually had the desired effect, but not before we had all been bored to sobs by having to overhear her.

Hunt staff wear sparkling white (not for long, but that's hounds for you) kennel coats and black bowler hats; I wonder that hounds recognise them sometimes. Judges, who are luminaries from other hunts, wear dark suits and bowlers if gentlemen, and smart suits and hats if ladies. Any judge not fitting into precisely those categories may choose one or the other, according to how much gossip they like to cause. There are two judges, and their methods are not at all what we are familiar with in lurcher and terrier shows, or Kennel Club showing, come to that.

Hound puppies are usually between six and ten months old when shown, so the older ones can have quite an advantage over the younger. First, all the doghounds come into the ring, which is square, like show rings and boxing rings, and has a central setting of flagstones so that feet can be seen clearly. Hounds are encouraged to move around and show themselves by a judicious use of biscuits. At this point, those spectators who are sitting in the front row realise why everyone else is sitting further back, because a doghound cocking its leg can only pee as far as the first row of seats. Then the little group is taken out, and doghound puppies are brought back in, two or three at a time, to be examined by the judges, and the huntsman gives out each hound's name when they come in. Judges are very concerned with good feet and general movement, hounds being kept moving by their huntsman throwing more biscuits for them to chase, and then standing them up to show off their conformation by more dextrous use of biscuits. The whipper-in has the task of shooing the more static hounds into action, and sometimes prying the more enthusiastic away from their puppy-walkers if they have seen them among the spectators. On occasion, an enterprising hound hurdles the fence and goes off in search of the tea tent, or else puts its nose down and leaves home after something alluring, whereupon the whipper-in has to split him- or herself in two and go after the miscreant hound while still fulfilling duties in the ring. With luck, there will be others about for pursuing errant hounds, but it isn't a given.

Judges look hard at hound conformation, but do not examine mouths and teeth closely, unlike our lurcher and terrier judges. I was surprised at first, but then I suppose only one hound catches the fox, mink or hare, and staghounds don't get hold of their quarry at all, so pack hounds do not need so tidy a mouth as a dog that catches rabbit after rabbit (and other creatures, pre-ban) or one that has to fence with a fox underground. That's just my way of working things out: there may be other reasons, and I would be interested to hear them if any hound judge would like to enlighten me. Of course I am aware that no hound catches anything any more, but they were judged in exactly the same way before the ban, when they did their proper task. The other big difference is that lurcher and terrier judges run their hands over the dogs they judge, where a hound judge does not touch hounds at all: the inspection is purely visual. A lesser difference is that it does not appear to matter if a hound is out of coat, in season, or just past it and in false pregnancy, therefore in soft condition, and that capped hocks and elbows or sore patches of skin do not seem to be considered important, whereas our lurchers and terriers are shown hard fit, spotlessly clean and ready to work. I am not saying that one is better than the other, simply highlighting the differences, which are intriguing. Similarities include the importance of good feet and general conformation, with hounds showing their movement at liberty, which latter is something we cannot do with our lurchers and terriers. Most lurchers would refuse to chase a biscuit, and many terriers would find a reason to fight over it, but hounds, being bred for centuries to live and work in packs, are more mellow about such things.

Once the doghounds have been looked over and the judges have marked their notes, the whole lot comes in again, and is reduced in number one by one, the judges pointing and the whipper-in catching and removing the hound indicated each

time, until three are left. Sometimes, varying from pack to pack, these three are taken out of the ring and shown running about in a larger area, and sometimes they stay in the ring and the judges choose their first, second and third, announced in reverse order to heighten the suspense. We spectators nod wisely and mark our cards as if we knew all along.

After the doghounds, the bitchhounds come in as a group, then in couples and threes, and are judged similarly. Finally, the winning doghound is judged against the winning bitch for the overall champion. Bitches tend to mature earlier than dogs, so this is not always an easy task. One recent puppy show nearly had an extra attraction added to the usual format as the winning bitch hound was in the later stages of her season, and the winning doghound was quite keen on doing something about that. Biscuits were produced, and I remember thinking "surely he won't be bought off by biscuits" but he was, which shows you something else you couldn't do in a terrier show, albeit possibly with a few lurchers.

Once the puppies have been judged, there can be a few 'extras' such as the best of last season's new entry, and the best overall hound in the pack, being paraded for us to admire. This is a matter of great pride for puppy-walkers when they see their puppies going on to become useful hounds. It must be dispiriting if your hound puppies are drafted or disappear for other reasons, but nobody talks about that. Judges meanwhile have a well-deserved break, for judging is always a tough task, whether hounds or other canines.

Prior to judges judging, they are invited to lunch, for puppy shows traditionally start at 3pm, and there have been occasions in the past where - good heavens - the show has started late. This breach of etiquette has traditionally occurred because judges are over-refreshed from luncheon, and have to be returned to judging mode by, one presumes, cold water, ice cubes, or homespun nostrums possibly involving Worcester sauce and something nasty from the flesh-house. Eventually they totter out, looking either parchment-coloured or rosy, and most manage to rally and do their job, though I do recall one, many years ago now who ... didn't. Still, the other judge did a good enough job for two. This is much less likely to occur in lurcher and terrier shows, as with the sterling exception of a very few clubs, there is more chance of the judges expiring from thirst and starvation than ever having a surfeit of refreshment. Thinking back over many years, I can recollect an occasional judge who was less sober than he should have been, but that was due to his own private refreshment rather than anything laid on by the organisers. I do also remember one who was handbagged out of the ring mid-show by a furious ex, as it was supposed to be his day for having the children, and I doubt you'd ever see that at a hunt puppy show if only because, in the best traditions of the upper classes, nobody seems to know for certain or worry much about whose children are whose anyway.

After hounds leave the ring, one of the Masters makes a speech of thanks to the judges and we all clap politely - just a little smattering, nothing over the top. Usually one, sometimes both, judges will thank the Hunt for inviting them, and if they have judged for this Hunt before, which most have, given the number of kennels and paucity of suitable judges, they will mention something suitably complimentary about the breeding of the pack, (especially if this involves doghounds from other packs with which the judge has connections) and how smart the kennels look, what fine fettle hounds are in, and what jolly good eggs we all are. We all believe this when we hear it. As a departure from the years of my youth, there is then a short political speech of the rallying kind, which is again followed by more polite clapping. After that, the ritual of The Joke. One of the judges tells it, and it is one of the trickiest moments of the day, not only because of side-bets taken on whether the judge will get to the end of it unscathed and remember the punchline (we all have had moments like that I am sure, and it gets worse as we get older. Venerable judges who have no fear of judging fine hounds can lie awake nights over The Joke) but also because The Joke has to be adequately funny, sufficiently decent that it does not enlighten the children or shock the ladies, and sufficiently smutty to make the chaps chuckle. It's quite a challenge.

Polite laughter follows The Joke, and then the judges can relax: their part in the proceedings is over apart from being collared by boring people (every hunt has some) over tea. But before the famished can get to the trough, we have Presentations. Into the ring is carried a table, to be covered by a dazzling white cloth, even whiter than the kennel coats, and a Person of Significance in the Hunt prepares to present prizes. Each puppy walker of each winning hound gets a trophy, usually a rather splendid silver cup, and often there is a silver teaspoon, engraved glass or other memento, and a framed photograph of their hound. Every puppy walker also gets these latter mementoes, which are very well received, and as each comes up in turn, there is more polite applause. Sometimes a child is sent to collect the prize, which is quite an ordeal for some, and a chance to show off for others. I have seen shy or sulky ones expertly propelled into the ring on the end of an auntly or grandmotherly knuckle, and the odd little extrovert who has to be propelled out again. After the puppy walkers' prizes, there may be the odd presentation to a retiring Master, a follower who has reached a significant birthday (and let's face it - every birthday is an achievement for those who ride horses across country after a pack of hounds) or a venerated pillar of the Hunt who has done something

admirable that the rest of us should be grateful for (and we are, believe me).

And then the faithful are summoned for tea. More properly: TEA. Hunt teas are incredible. Everyone who can do so brings home-made goodies, and my word can these people cook. Any television chef would be overcome at the variety and excellence of the spread, usually laid out in a marquee with a few volunteers batting off wasps, stray children, and the odd escaped hound or terrier (how do they get there? But they always do). Because we are English, we form an orderly queue while hunt supporters who are Tribal Elders, and officiate at all such occasions, pour strong no-nonsense tea from strong no-nonsense teapots. According to our capricious summer weather, the tea tent may have to be held down in a gale, huddled under in a downpour, have the flames beaten out after a lightning strike while we all wonder if we are safer inside it or out, or is as hot as a camel's armpit on a sunny day in the desert. The last option may have an uncertain effect on some of the more susceptible ingredients in the spread of goodies, but to my knowledge no guest has ever developed a significant intestinal disturbance (which just shows how tough hunting people can be). During tea, there is a parade of hounds, the poor whipper-in having to work very hard indeed at keeping the thieving four-footed contingent away from (most of) the food, while his by now overstressed huntsman plans exactly what he is going to say to him once they are both safely out of earshot. Meanwhile, networking is networked, reputations are shattered or salvaged, scurrilous gossip is exchanged and characters are assassinated. Certain folk are able to discuss what is on their minds and others can practice their listening skills while endeavouring not to look as bored as they feel.

Some of the tea is enhanced by diplomatic wafts of a whisky bottle. There goes the judge again.

After the main body of the supporters has drifted off to milk cows, get horses in and see to all the other teatime tasks that rule the country-dweller, the Inner Circle gathers. A party of Lucullan proportions spreads and grows in the immediate vicinity of the huntsman's house, and will probably be going past midnight and well into the dawn. What goes on there stays down there, not so much from duplicity as amnesia. And that is that until the Puppy Show next year. I wouldn't miss it for the world, and if you get an invitation, make sure you go. It's worth getting togged up in your best 'whistle' just to be part of a superb tradition. Nobody does it quite so well as we do.

Photo: Janet George

Ten

High Horses

YOU might think an Irish Draught is a pint of stout, but in fact it is a horse the size of a block of flats and with the acceleration and turning circle of a fighter aircraft. Four of them bore down on us at mach one, bucking and farting and sliding about on the wet grass. My lurcher hid behind my legs and suggested I Do Something And Do It Now. My friend had, with great presence of mind, picked up the ferret boxes and removed himself to the far side of a gate that was suddenly looking very flimsy. Fortunately, we hadn't put any nets down, and the only catch so far was a rabbit that the Colly had picked up as we'd trudged over to the buries. It looked as if another ferreting day had gone to rat ordure.

The owner had either forgotten that we were ferreting, or maybe thought it wouldn't matter as she released these monster horses into the field. They were friendly in an overbearing kind of way, likely to send you flying with a shove from a head the size of a coffin if they didn't tread you into a divot by accident, and with that slapstick sense of humour favoured by large herbivores. Discreetly, I removed dog, nets and then myself from the field, while the horses ranged up and down the fenceline, snorting steam from nostrils the size of pint pots.

Photo: Janet George

I try to avoid ferreting in fields with livestock in them. I know people with lurchers that are very handy at rounding up or sending away, but I would rather mine did not get involved. Sometimes the livestock creeps up on you while you are occupicd with net-setting, or waiting for bolters, and the first you know is that warm bubbly breath on the back of

*Photo:
Janet
George*

Photo: Janet George

Photo: Janet George

your neck, which can cause other unwanted warmth from the shock. Cattle like to eat nets and terrorise the dog, while sheep try to join in the spirit of the occasion by finding holes to put their feet down. Horses, dangerous at both ends and more expensive than other stock if damaged, favour the frontal approach.

We decamped to the front drive where, if you didn't mind working through a fence, a ditch and quite a bit of blackthorn, rabbits might be caught, but it wasn't half as much fun for the Colly, and really I only go ferreting to give her entertainment. Still, we plugged away, topping up our tetanus from the rusty wire and the thorns, and our leptospirosis from the ditchwater. Inevitably there was a 'water over the boot' moment; very refreshing it was too.

Twenty-two hard-won rabbits later, we packed up and went to tell the landowners we had finished and offer them their usual brace of the best rabbits. They are nice people, and were disappointed that we had ferreted the drive and not the big field; they had turned the horses out there, but knew they wouldn't have bothered us. True enough, the horses were now grazing peacefully, but we know that trick. We took another

walk across there, but stayed on the safe side of the fence and sure enough the horses came over to leap and kick out playfully at each other as close to us as they could manage. In our strategic withdrawal earlier, we had left the Colly's first rabbit on the horse side, so it would have been twenty-three rabbits if either of us had decided it was worth the excitement of collecting it. "Sometimes I wonder why I bother" she said, looking at us the way lurchers look.

Eleven

The Quiet Man

LURCHERS, being naturally well-mannered dogs, suffer more than many breeds from canine hooligans getting in their faces and spilling their beer. As their first line of defence is generally running away, by the time they resort to the second, which is spinning the bully over and pinning it, or else shaking the living ordure out of it, the thug owners tend not to understand why the dogs aren't playing nicely any more. Funny how owners of bullying dogs think they are 'playing' isn't it? If that's playing, I'd hate to see them when they get serious.

The Bedlington Thing's father, nineteen inches and nineteen pounds of beige fluff, endured nine months of harassment by a spaniel. It was a difficult situation as the spaniel belonged to his owner's employer. Eventually the pup became mature enough for his terrier genes to kick in and - listen, do you have any idea of what happens when Bedlingtons get miffed? Having prised his jaws open and extracted a considerable amount of spaniel, his owner was startled to hear: "Why did he do that? They've always been such good friends".

Years ago, listening to a shoot briefing with every dog on the lead except one, I watched a Labrador walking stiff-legged round the other dogs, intimidating each one in turn. Politely I asked the owner to call his dog, and was told, "He's all right".

Well, he very soon won't be, I thought, as he neared the Bedlington Thing. "You heard me say that", I said quietly to the gamekeeper, who knew better than many people what the little dog was like on foxes. Then I removed the lead. Suffice it that it took his dander a long time to come down again, and we never did find his rag, but I actually saw a 'keeper smile.

The gentle Worm was once savaged by a Dobermann that was still on the lead, causing me to use some unfortunate language as I struggled to part them, Dobermanns being slippery and with little to get hold of apart from their ears. We also had a spell of having to avoid a farm Labrador and her owner, who were dead ringers in the ratbag stakes. The larger of the two bitches point-blank refused to keep her dog under control, which gave me a difficult time protecting my lurcher, as I had to be there twice a day and I never knew when the two of them would turn up. But one glorious winter evening, that same Labrador came barrelling round the corner in the dark, and pitched into the fawn bitch by mistake. Schadenfreud is so good sometimes.

This fawn bitch was a quiet dog, but she gave road to none, even when past her youth. It was this same lurcher who used regularly to have to endure a terrier that would charge up and run all round her, yapping and snarling, while she stared into the middle distance with regal disdain. One day the terrier became over-confident and latched onto her. It had a bit of a

squeeze and a flying lesson, and crawled away chastened but unharmed apart from bruises. The owner, who made as much noise as her dog at the time, has never spoken to me since.

A quiet man of my acquaintance was walking with his elderly lurcher at heel, and his greyhound, which was devoted to her, gambolling about as fit greyhounds do. Then one of those brown furry long-eared things hopped past, and the greyhound gambolled right over the hill after it, and out of sight. Meantime, a Dobermann "with one of them fancy collars" appeared and began to harass the old dog. Upon asking the owner to call her dog away, he was told that it was only playing. Realising he was in the same airspace as an idiot, and not being given to wasting his breath, he walked on quickly, but the Dobermann continued to pester, getting progressively bolder as it dived and snapped at the frail old dog. Over the hill came the greyhound at a fair lick, and clocked the situation. Take one eighty pound dog travelling at thirty miles an hour, factor in the gradient, the curvature of the earth and a complete lack of slowing down and you will

understand something of the force with which the greyhound hit the Dobermann. While it was on the ground yelling, it had its neck nuzzled in a companionable way, which ripped the fancy collar right off. Then the greyhound came to heel, for it was a well-trained dog, and the Dobermann fled back to its owner. "Mine don't play", said the quiet man, as he walked on with his dogs at heel behind him.

Twelve

Puppies and Papers

THE litter that gave me the Black Death (the pup not the disease - although I do wonder sometimes) is the last one I intend to breed, but of course being a woman, I can change my mind. The floor is getting further away, and raising puppies properly is a lot of hard work, followed by experiences I could just as soon do without when it's time to home them. Mine have always previously been booked before they were born, but last time around I had two that I had to advertise, and encountered the customary messers and timewasters that this process attracts, as well as some really nice people who simply would not have been capable of managing the prey drive in the dogs I breed. They have all turned out well, they are doing their job, and while I really miss those small-puppy moments (you know: before the teeth and legs come through, and they run about biting you) I won't miss the work.

Other breeds that decently have dinky little litters of half a dozen or so do not prepare anyone for the sheer volume of puppery that a lurcher or sighthound bitch can produce. Similarly with the colossal amount of body waste that a big litter creates, the shortest interval of time known to man being that between a puppy pooping and treading in it. If pups can get out of the nest to empty themselves, they do so at an amazingly early age, but that still means an insane amount of newspaper if you are keeping them decently clean. After begging friends and even slight acquaintances to save their papers, you find that still isn't enough, and respectable people are sometimes seen at dead of night, flitting between the recycling bins put out for emptying the next day, extracting newspaper.

I know of two ladies of impeccable background who, having exhausted the local bins and freebie papers, were observed early one morning at a major supermarket outlet, liberating the contents of the vast paper-recycling container. One, being tall and slender, discovered that she could actually get into the bin and so pass the papers down to her accomplice beneath, from whence they were stowed in the kind of vehicle more used to guns and fishing rods. This was all going well, when an Officer of the Law appeared. Yes, some upright citizen had reported a theft! Now then, what's goin' on 'ere?

Blushing, breathless and apologetic, as any of us might be if caught up to our knees in a recycling bin, one criminal asked the O of the L if indeed this was worthy of their attention, and the copper, trying heroically not to snigger said that, sadly, helping yourselves to newspapers that had been thrown away was actually considered theft. But, said the lovely lady breathlessly, we have sixteen Labrador puppies between us! And they are six weeks old - and they are getting through so much newspaper ...

The O of the L, still with an almost straight face, said that, being as the thieves seemed the sort of people who didn't normally get into trouble with the police, he was willing to let them off this time provided the lady standing in the bin got out of it and they both shoved off right this minute. He even managed not to notice the pile of newspaper already in the car. Mind you, he added thoughtfully, it would be very tempting to nick you two, even if only to see the reaction back at the Station. Whereupon he gave up trying to look stern, saw them off the premises, and drove off, chuckling.

I would like to thank the ladies concerned for allowing me to use this story. They don't breed dogs any more either.

Thirteen

Beaten

SOME field sports experiences stick in your mind for ever, and one vivid memory is the season I spent beating on a smart driven shoot. I'll try most things once: I have been an enthusiastic participant in foxhunting, mounted and foot, all types of lurcher and terrier work, ratting, ferreting, lamping, bobbery packery, coursing, general mooching along hedgerows and waterways, beagling, mink hunting, and the only reason I have never been stag - or hindhunting with a mounted pack is geographical. I have qualified horses for point-to-points, ridden in them and raced on the Flat as well, and in the course of all this outdoor fun have been cold, wet and uncomfortable for many hours at a time, taking it all as a part of the whole.

But there is one experience that left me scarred for life, and in terms of human endurance, nothing else with the exception of Fell hunting comes anywhere near it. Those of you who shoot the high, curling pheasants, the screaming coveys of partridges, the darting woodcock (thank goodness I never experienced grouse moors) have you ever dedicated one half of a thought about how the blasted things are persuaded to appear in front of you?

It was unseemly for one of my years and general decrepitude to have even considered beating, and I can only plead a moment's inattention and a slack spell at work, fuelled by a deliberate fudging of essential information from those who should know better. I had, I admit, very little knowledge about what was involved, though I knew a number of people who went beating regularly and said they really enjoyed it. I did consider signing up with the anti brigade if only because the pay was better, but the thought of all those lentils in a confined space put me off, and I never could see myself in an anorak anyway.

So when those I thought were friends suggested I came along for what apparently was going to be a terrific experience full of fun and camaraderie, I was totally taken in. I asked what we had to do, and was told we just had to keep in line and follow the gamekeeper's instructions. Sounds easy enough, doesn't it? A stroll through the woods, the odd cry of 'Brrrr' (I practiced - I could Brrr away with the best) tapping with your stick when told, being quiet when required, a permitted sharp alarm call when inadvertently descending a slope that I should have been ascending - nothing to tax the grey matter there. Fortunately for me, the 'keeper was one of the sort who, despite the stress of a shoot day, displayed reserves of calm and self-control that would do credit to anyone. Many an apoplectic Field-Master could have learned much from him. Only once in the whole season did I see him lose his temper, and that under severe provocation that luckily had nothing to do with the newest beater.

That first time I realised that everybody else was younger, or else taller with longer legs. Despite pre-shoot-day assurances from my vile acquaintances that there were allowances made for the old and feeble, it became very clear from the get-go that this was no place for anyone who wasn't as fit as a marathon runner. My progress through undergrowth more suited to terriers became surreal as I struggled through that which everyone else could step over, observing in the process that hawthorn was nastier than bramble, blackthorn hurt more, and wild rose had more arresting power than all of them (you

could use that stuff on an aircraft carrier, I reckon). In fact, the restrictive capabilities of wild briar on a vertically-challenged decrepit old biddy were exceeded only by the cables of Old Man's Beard, albeit less painfully. Thorn thicket inserted fingers down my collar and painfully into my ears (I learned to take my earrings out before we started) stopping me dead, like a beetle on its back, all flailing legs and going nowhere. There were many times when I thought I was going to spend the rest of my life handcuffed to some ruddy triffid, and that was without the rigours of the stock-fencing with two strands of barbed wire on top, which claimed quite a lot of my clothing over the season. What put the cream on the whole experience, though, was the gradient.

I am a lowlander by birth and nurture. These hills were colossal to me. Often after a drive, another beater would comment on the fine scenery or the quality of the shooting, but all I ever saw was my feet, or sometimes my fingertips, as I struggled for a hold on the kind of surfaces more suitable for Spiderman. Apart from the pains in my lungs and legs, there was the stark terror caused by my fear of heights, which was apparently shared by the pheasants as they sneaked up the

hill in front of us, cheeping softly in worried tones. I can assure you that the saturation theory does not work: I am still scared of heights. I was amazed to be asked to come again after my multiple displays of ineptitude, but I think our 'keeper was working on the theory that half a beater was better than none.

What can you remember from past seasons? Memories that stay with me apart from the pain, the fear and the way everything stings in the bath afterwards, were diverse. The pale hen pheasant that peeped at me from out of a rabbit-hole, the drive where the beaters' dogs' tally almost exceeded that of the Guns, the Gun who had shot like a hero all day and who came and thanked us beaters at the end of it, one of only two who did so all season, the big man working a spaniel and a flatcoat alternately, whose dogs performed with a quiet brilliance all day. Alas, I can also remember the incredible stinging power of tiny nettles, the fallen beech tree that was taller than me and over the slippery trunk of which I had to climb every single time we were out, trying to cross streams and ditches that were always wider than my stumpy legs could reach, and the unfailing inevitability of finishing a drive at the top of a hill when we needed to be at the bottom of another for the next drive except for when we finished at the foot of a hill and needed to start again at the top of the next. I beat for the whole season on the grounds that you can't judge anything from one or two attempts at it, and now and again through that winter I enquired of the Sahib at what stage I would actually begin to enjoy it, or what indeed there was to enjoy. Being younger, taller and having lungs like a blacksmith's bellows, he could not understand why I wasn't loving every anaerobic moment. I've ridden horses that acted like helicopters, I've walked-up hares across plough that reached almost to my knees and felt like half a county on each boot, and I've had one season's beating. It was years ago, but I can still remember it with awful clarity. It may have been a kindness to all concerned that I never went again, but at least I know how those birds are sent across to the waiting Guns now.

Fourteen

Guns and Noses

WHEN I first met the Sahib (lady with lurchers requires gentleman with vermin), he was used to shooting over his ferrets, while I worked them with a lurcher. Never were there two more conflicting ways to conduct the same discipline: he was convinced that a dog anywhere near the buries would lead to rabbits refusing to bolt, and I was afraid my ferrets would be shot by accident. I used a dog to check if there were rabbits in the buries, and he used fieldcraft. I thought the dog was better and he thought it would be a something liability, bound to be off slaughtering deer and pheasants when not tied to a tree, or crunching the rabbits to shrapnel if any ever did bolt despite it pushing its head down the rabbit-holes, not to mention the constant barking. He wasn't convinced that his ferrets would be safe from a mauling, either.

So he took me ferreting his way, using his ferrets because after all, we'd only just met and men like to think they know best, and I was pleasantly surprised not only at his fieldcraft but his safety-consciousness. The ferrets were in no danger, and it was all rather restful with no netting up. We sat in a cleft on one hillside with the ferrets working buries on the other: safe backdrop and rabbits bolting nicely. After the action stopped and the ferrets came out, we wandered down and picked up the slain rabbits, then set off to the next bury with no time lost collecting nets again. But when next time I wanted to show him how to ferret my way, he told me he preferred to purse-net if he wasn't shooting, and didn't want to know about the lurcher work at all. Being adult about these things, we compromised by working different buries on the same hill.

At the time, I was fielding Worm, a lurcher of such apologetic and gentle demeanour that it was hard to believe she could ever catch anything. However, she was the perfect pot-filler, turning her paw to feather and fur of every sort, and adaptable over any country. She showed me a bury with rabbits present, and I started setting nets, never doubting her ability because she was never wrong. Before long, we were extracting a steady tally of rabbits, the dog obligingly holding them in the nets until I could get to them. She was velvet-mouthed, and never marked a rabbit in all her life.

After an hour or so, the Sahib's bury had yielded up its contents successfully with no help from a skinny cur, so he came round to see how I was doing. I suspect he was surprised at the neat line of cooling rabbits and the dog watching the bury quietly instead of crunching them or dragging them about. I offered to show him exactly what we did with the next bury, and he came along to humour me. He watched her mark so that I knew the bury was occupied, helped me set

the nets, and frowned as the dog trod lightly around, testing the air at the rabbit holes but not scrabbling or snorting down them as he had thought she would. Then in went the ferrets and he saw Worm back off to one side of the bury, flicking her ears and flaring her nostrils as she felt the ferrets working below from vibrations under her feet, scenting and listening all the time. He could hardly contain his disapproval when she walked right across the bury to stand next to a rabbit hole, not pushing her face at it, but even so where she would surely scare any rabbit trying to bolt. A round fluffy face peered cautiously out of the rabbit hole: the dog froze. The rabbit hopped once and paused, feeling the net. The dog didn't move. The rabbit launched itself and so did the dog: all the human eye could see was a dog standing still, then a dog floating gently back to earth with a rabbit in her mouth. I was used to this: he wasn't. I took the rabbit, which the dog released straight away like good ferreting dogs do, and then we had two rabbits bolt from different holes. The dog caught one and I had the other. I was just disentangling the second net when another rabbit shot out of a hidden pop-hole, and the dog, which had soundlessly arranged herself in exactly the right place, lurched forward and closed her jaws around it and then carried it back to me, her eyes glowing with pride.

Once that bury was empty, he helped me pick up the nets and box the ferrets while conceding that a dog could possibly have its uses after all.

Twenty years or so later, he is still a tad frosty about the early training of a ferreting dog, where they do get it wrong until they have learned to stand off and let the rabbits bolt. We are now fielding Worm's great-great granddaughter, every bit as much of an asset as all her predecessors, and we also shoot over ferrets without a dog when the land is more suitable for that. But that first time had one more speciality of the running dog to teach him, and one that I had never trained her to do. Once we had finished with the bury, we went to get the rabbits to paunch them out, and they seemed to have grown in number. This often happens ferreting my way, when you get so involved in the bolting and re-netting that you lose track of how many you have caught. There isn't a gun in the world, though, that can replicate a thieving lurcher. We both realised at the same time what had been happening, as Worm came round the hill carrying the last of the rabbits that the Sahib had caught by himself, and left tidily on the bury awaiting his return. She stashed it with the ones we had caught together, gave us a huge lurcher grin and wagged her tail.

Fifteen

The Magic Drain

THE magic drain can make a fool out of an experienced team, or else bring undreamed-of results. It is Y-shaped, and when things go as they should, the terrier enters the long arm of the Y, the lurcher stands between the two short arms, and the gun acts as long-stop if the fox bolts over the terrier and exits by the long end. The farm it was on was heavily over-foxed because the outlying fields had been sold off for building, and now housing estates stood where once we had done a great deal of our hunting. The folk there fed the foxes that came into their gardens, and after an appetising snack of unsuitable food, these foxes would come across the farm in search of something to top up with. This caused the farm manager grief, and us great pleasure.

The farm manager did not like longdogs, and I was on a kind of perpetual probation, only allowed there on sufferance, and due to his long friendship with the Sahib and his father before him. Oh yes, and because we knocked over appreciable numbers of rabbits and foxes. The farm itself was like the enchanted Guinness bottle, eternally refilling, and every few weeks there would be a new fox in the drain. We had ways of telling that each fox was a new one.

This particular time when we tried the drain hadn't been a success. We knew in our hearts that it was going to be a mistake as soon as one of us said 'let's take a look at that drain' when we were on our way home with a tired terrier, a tired lurcher, no nets and no gun. The terrier we had at that time had been read the Code of Conduct as a bedtime story, and had too strong a sense of self-preservation to mix it with a fox. Instead, she would bay in a most persuasive manner, pleading with the fox to leave its refuge. Some would say she was an arrant coward, but it worked well for us. Foxes sometimes pushed past her and bolted, anathema for the dyed-in-the-wool terrier men but just what we wanted, as neither of us was all that struck on digging, and you can't dig drains like this anyway. We wanted foxy to bolt, and foxy mostly did: if one was not too keen, we'd grab the terrier when she came out (oh yes, she was definitely a quitter) and withdraw to the hedgerow up the bank, which was fairly sheltered and afforded a good view. Presently we'd see a lithe russet shape ease out of the drain, and it was 'game on'. But not this day.

The first thing that went wrong was the terrier entering at one of the short arms of the drain before we could stop her. She gave mouth immediately, and I saw the Sahib sprinting up the field waving his cap at a departing fox. It jinked through the hedge and the fawn bitch was looking the wrong way. I couldn't believe it! She didn't miss foxes - but she sure as heck missed this one. The fox did a handbrake turn and shot back down the drain, straight over the top of the terrier. While breathless bumping noises went on in the drain, I hauled the lurcher out of the ditch where she was trying to follow the fox down the drain, and pointed her in the direction where I thought the fox was most likely to bolt. She then threw a major tantrum about my interfering. During the following full and frank exchange of views, the fox bolted again, which I saw and the lurcher didn't. When I say 'bolted' I actually mean the subtlest flowing of fox molecules, barely noticeable even when you are expecting it, rather than a cork-out-of-a-bottle moment. The fox caught my eyes with a 'why don't you lot just shove off?' kind of glare, and dropped back into the drain again. The terrier emerged with a 'did you get it?' expression, and we grabbed her before she could re-enter the drain.

A gathering of shattered nerves was in order for all parties, so we all did that, and then the Sahib said he'd go home, get his gun and the other lurcher, and we'd have another try. I was ordered to watch the drain and stop the fox departing, which was a tricky task until the shepherd's wife came by, and stopped to talk, which kept the fox firmly where it was.

The shepherd's wife was very keen for us to succeed, though I explained that the fawn bitch was not on song, possibly because she was due imminently in season. "I can identify with that," she said, "get her a velvet cushion and some chocolate!"

The Sahib was back in short order with reinforcements and his gun. The lurcher part was an unentered sapling, and it would be an ideal opportunity for him to run one with his mother, who was normally an excellent foxing dog. At that point, however, my usual confidence in her had been badly shaken. In went the terrier at the right end of the drain, out

popped foxy, who dived across the track and straight in again (is this beginning to sound familiar yet?) over the top of the terrier and straight out, to run the bottom of the ditch where only I could see it. Normally this is game over, but not this time. The fawn bitch followed my directions into the ditch, but missed where it had gone, while the sapling ran heel scent having gone in unsighted, and tried to cram himself down the drain. The terrier hurtled out of the ditch and ran screeching (her version of baying was a banshee scream) in the right direction, the fawn bitch ran to holloa and was rapidly overhauling the terrier when the Sahib coolly shot the fox abeam him as it tried to go through the hedge. The dogs then had a good rag at the carcase while I muttered darkly about none of them having earned it.

Luckily for my dented pride, the magic drain never stayed untenanted for long, and it was a bare month later when we had another look, this time 'going equipped'. The fawn bitch was on song, the terrier played a blinder, the gun stayed unfired and we had a fine result, but that doesn't make half such a good story.

Sixteen

From the Southern End of a Northbound Bull

SUMMER is the season for country shows, game fairs, lurcher and terrier shows and more bull than you'll find in a tin of corned beef. Being a woman, it is a given that I know nothing about fieldsports, and I seem to be a magnet for people who talk utter bollards. Listening to them with a straight face is something I regard as charity work.

There's the chap who regaled me with tales of his deer-coursing exploits, and at a time when I was in possession (as one 'keeper put it) of 'the best deer dog in Sussex'. His tales grew wilder and more colourful as I stood with the aforementioned hound beside me, and I swear she sniggered when he got to the bit about breaking a fallow buck's neck by twisting its head around by its antlers (accompanied by the actions, a bit like Swing Low Sweet Chariot). It was pretty obvious that the nearest he had ever been to an antlered buck was sitting under a stuffed head at the pub. The same dog was dismissed by a 'real dogman' for apparently having a weak neck and therefore being no good for anything except rabbits. Tell that to the lady with five freezers. Then there was the so-say Romany gypsy (aren't they all) who scattered his speech with Romany words to convince me of his authenticity. He ticked me off for saying that I let my lurcher walk over the bury when ferreting. This, he told me sternly, would stop the rabbits from bolting. Eyeing my pale fawn dog, he added that no true hunter would keep a dog that colour because it showed up so much. As I frequently appreciate the camouflage of my various pale fawn dogs when we are out mooching, I could maybe be excused for suspecting that he had not done quite as much lurcher work as he made out.

I have been informed that any dog used regularly on foxes will be heavily marked up, which did make me wonder what the peppery-smelling ginger fluffy-tailed creatures were that my dogs kept catching, and which mostly had no choice but to give up the ghost before they could bite at all. It is true that the Bedlington Thing has a few scars, but these are mostly caused by his habit of assuming that if you hit any obstacle hard enough, it will get out of the way. He tried it with a perfectly obvious oak tree once, which did him no good at all,

A load of bull!

and his most impressive scar is from a sheet of corrugated iron that some pillock dumped in a wood. As he was after a fox at the time, I suppose it could be loosely termed a fox scar. Of all my dogs, he is the one that has sustained the most fox bites, largely due to his knack of catching them in the middle of vast bramble patches, but you wouldn't call him marked-up. Then I had it explained to me that he was too small to catch foxes, so that told me, then.

I have heard of Alsatians that coursed and caught hares regularly, as (apparently) did an Akita. There was the greyhound that caught twenty-nine rabbits in thirty minutes, and I may have failed my maths '0' level but even I can do that sum, chum, and you'm do be talkin' gruntfuttocks, unless you forgot to mention you shot them first. Lads that weren't even a twinkle in their daddy's eye when I started hunting tell me you need a big heavy dog for deer and foxes, that saluki crosses are stupid, deerhound crosses are clumsy, and that extraordinary things happen when you put a house brick in a ferret hutch. In the latter case, I think some people spend too much time on their own down the allotment.

I like the shows: I like to see different sorts of lurcher, and I enjoy the craic. But please spare me the trips to Fantasy Island, because I won't respect you in the morning, even if you did lamp a hundred rabbits last night.

Seventeen

The Terrierist

THE young terrier has not yet learned to work in a methodical manner, nor as part of a pack. She travels at an extended hurtle, smashing through the thickest cover without flinching. She's like a cocker on speed. The lurchers, used to steadier terriers, find her a tad exasperating. Once she steadies down and sticks to working in the same county as the rest of us, she's going to be a gem.

I like to work terriers and lurchers together, but you need a sense of humour and properly trained dogs. It helps if one of you works the terriers, and another the lurchers. And you have to be adaptable, because each one has a favoured method of working, and you're better to go with it than against it. It's true you sometimes get a lurcher working thick cover and a terrier bouncing about outside

waiting for the bolt: it happened again yesterday and I saw a terrific course. The terrier is about the same size as a good rabbit, and she flattened her ears and pelted after it, little legs a blur, then took the most amazing flying leap and seized the coney halfway along the back. It was as good a catch as I've seen any dog make. My old lurcher, who had been working the cover, emerged in a halo of dangling greenery, confiscated the rabbit and retrieved it to me. Had the terrier not let go, he would have retrieved her as well. We still have some work to do there, but what the hell.

Up on the hillside, where there are huge patches of thick thorn cover, dense scrub and strange ferns, it is like the Home Counties equivalent of the Amazon Basin. Anyone old enough to remember Michael Bentine's flea circus would be helpless with laughter watching small wriggles in the vegetation being followed by large wriggles. There is gasping and the odd yip (damned noisy terrier at home, but silent working unless she is right on a rabbit's scut), and starbursts of departing blackbirds telling us where the little wossname is now. A rabbit slides across a bare patch followed by a terrier running hard with nose down, and lurchers dance around bramble heaps like Essex girls around handbags. Sometimes I intervene with my stick, or wade through waist-high nettles in obedience to a stout mark by a lurcher that would like to know when we will be getting a terrier that is actually on hand when needed. Every now and then there is a frantic note to the scuffling, sometimes followed by a squeal and a shaking of undergrowth, or else a bolt that is generally a rabbit of some sort. Then you see lurchers lurch, for these two, father and daughter, have learned to work quarry between them, and very little that gets out in the open makes it to safety these days. Meanwhile, the terrier gallops across to a large puddle, drinks copiously, wees in the water (why do they do that?) and collapses grinning onto her belly, legs out fore and aft and a tongue a yard long. A couple of minutes' R and R and she'll be off again. Now, where are those lurchers?

Eighteen

Country Estate

IT'S a morning's work to prepare a lurcher-car for the MOT, at least if you want to give it a fighting chance, the alternative being to divert a small river through it. It has been known as the 'auxhall' since I had to make a split-second decision between a gatepost and a ditch while out lamping, and is the nearest I'll ever get to a country estate. Plenty of topsoil, anyway, and sufficient algae growing around most of the rubbery bits to look like a lawn.

Inside, there is enough sprouting grain to satisfy the most demanding vegan, and at certain times of year, toadstools bob unexpectedly and luminously in the footwells. Insulation is provided by a thick layer of dog hair and the odd cobweb. I don't bother the spider and it doesn't bother me except sometimes when it lowers itself on a string from the sun visor, and once during a traffic jam on the A303, when it built half a web between my hand and the steering-wheel before we got moving again. Privacy here doesn't mean blacked-out windows but dog-snotted ones, and there's no point cleaning them because the dogs can snot faster than I can wipe. Then of course, there is the Smell.

I don't mean the smell of dog, because that's a given with a working car that is regularly full of wet muddy hounds. I

mean the haunting notes of rabbit musk overlaid with ferret, and the strong, peppery huff of fox. Intermingled with the 'regulars' you get the occasional interloper, such as the result of an altercation with a stoat or mink (don't knock it till you've tried it) or the unfortunate aftermath of the forgotten pigeon under the seat. Strange small mummified objects that are best not investigated too closely add their own magic to the more recent tragedies such as the pup that rolled in – precisely what is it badgers eat that causes that?

Forensics should train on cars like mine. Tyres are stained with the piss of a thousand farm curs, and there is often something organic deep in the tread. Blood from many sources, hair and feathers from more, small religious relics of various denominations, the dent from the deer that came round suddenly in the back*, and the corrosive effects of all sorts of body fluids would provide enough challenge for anyone. Maybe the Institute of Tropical Diseases should give it a go as well: I do get quite a few mosquitos but that may be due to small areas of standing water that I haven't found yet. Mind you, the spider keeps the minor stuff under control, and the dogs apprehend anything from fly size upwards except for those flat brown sideways-hopping biting things you get on pigeons – at the first bzzzzt! everyone is in the front seat with me, and I'm scrabbling at the door handle to get out.

Anyway, the thick layer of dust has been re-arranged, and I've removed the useful sacks for putting things in, the old sheets and blankets for covering them over once I've put them in there, the graft, swap-hook, long-handled shears and thumbsticks (two) the locator collar I've had the drains up looking for, and a handful of slip-leads. It will take me ages, well at least a week, to get the car back the way I need it.

should anyone accuse me of unsportsmanlike or indeed illegal actions, I would like to point out that the deer was a roadkill – or rather a roadstun. It wasn't half lively once it woke up, and I had the dickens of a job persuading it to get out.

Nineteen

Ratting

RATTING in the cover-crops was a new experience for me, and I was fortunate to be invited to go out with this established team. The briefing was short: no sticks, no guns, no strange dogs, and let the dogs catch the rats. This was sensible, for here was no place for shooting, and lashing out with sticks and boots can cause injury to dogs and people. While it was a pity not to be able to bring a dog or two, I could understand the regular team's concerns over strange dogs about which they knew nothing. We met on a bitterly cold day, and I was wearing so many layers of clothing that it was amazing I could walk (details upon request). Most important were the stout boots and gaiters, for a rat up the trouser leg is not everyone's idea of fun, though I suppose it would be extra warmth, especially if accompanied by a terrier.

The terriers, a couple of dozen of them, consisted of various Lakelands, Borders, a smart quartet of Plummers and the rest an assortment loosely covered by the term "Jack Russell". They milled about eyeing each other up for weakness and the potential for a fight, except for a very introverted Border, who wanted nothing to do with the other dogs and came shyly round the humans for kind words and stroking. The people were just as varied (though nobody wanted stroking), with a hardcore of experienced vermin despatchers, and a sprinkling of children, including one babe in a backpack, and a lad in his early teens demonstrating how well'ard he was by wearing only a teeshirt and combats. One of our number, my friend Buck, was allocated heavy-duty gloves and a large sack, which was the rat-bag.

The terriers spilled into the remains of the cover-crop at one end, and started marking at once. There certainly were plenty of rat-holes. The smoker started with a roar and a gout of stinking smoke, down the nearest rat-hole went the tube, and the terriers arranged themselves eagerly for the bolts. They did not have long to wait: out shot a rat, various people commented on this, and terriers were galvanised into action. A brief skirmish, and an ex-rat went into the bag. One terrier bloodied, and a raise in tempo for all.

Though terriers worked regularly as a pack tend to split into 'find' dogs and 'catch' dogs, some of these terriers proved

excellent at both marking and catching, and some did nothing in particular except scurry about and enjoy themselves by annoying other terriers. It also became apparent that, if you want your terrier to work as part of a trencher-fed pack, avoid calling it Ruby, Rosie or Jack, because most of them seemed

to be called one of these, and so every time somebody yelled for their terrier, they irritated several others. The terriers themselves settled down quite quickly into a formidable working pattern, and I was amazed that they could continue marking so well in the stench of the smoker. Some rats refused to bolt and were dug out by eager paws, occasionally assisted with a graft carefully wielded by a helpful human. It was tremendously exciting, especially when we had a multiple bolt, for the terriers did not have much space in which to catch before a rat took refuge underground again. I was very impressed by their overall good behaviour, particularly as, once they had killed, they had to relinquish the rat without argument to the holder of the rat-bag.

Though we had all received the same briefing, sundry people had still brought sticks, or tried to kill the rats by jumping on them, which on one occasion saw about fourteen stone of over-excited ratter jumping in the air and landing on my foot. It's almost better now, thank you for asking. But soon these people drifted away, leaving a hard core of dedicated ratters working in the freezing cold.

There was one outstanding terrier, and she would not have won any show class. Her head was too big for her body, with long pendulous ears. Her back was long, too, and she had Queen Anne front legs, being short-legged all round. Vaguely Jack Russell in type but maybe with a touch of Basset, she

almost had a broken coat, and was not in the first flush of youth. That terrier was a jewel: she marked staunchly and accurately, and as soon as the smoker was brought to honour the mark, she was away to stand in a rat-run and claim the rat. Though all the terriers were good, this one was head and shoulders above the rest, and I took to finding and watching her no matter where the main shifting mass of terriers was congregated.

We progressed in a methodical fashion, ratting at tree-roots and along fencelines, feed rides and more cover-crops, the terriers never slacking, though a few by now had sustained the odd rat-bite. The smoker gave up the ghost, and after a short cold delay, a new one was found, and meanwhile the temperature dropped further. The baby went home, and well'ard accepted a coat. Buck was finding the rat-bag heavy,

and the chill deepened towards sunset. A young lad asked Daddy if he was going to call it a day yet?

One more fenceline, and then the light really was going. Buck tipped out the rat-bag, and we counted over forty complete rats, plus several more in kit form. The terriers were still up for it, whatever 'it' was. I had really enjoyed the day as well; though I have done a fair bit of ratting, this was the first time I had been involved in this particular version, and also had the chance to watch a big terrier pack in action. I had had a wonderful time, and was very appreciative of being allowed to come along. Thank you all: you know who you are, and your terriers are marvellous.

Twenty

The Dangers of Lurchers

RELATIVELY few people can say that they have had their nose broken by a caterpillar, even if you factor in the involvement of a lurcher. It happened many years ago, when my friend and I were exercising our pack of running dogs and I saw this huge psychedelic catty undulating across the track. We both bent over for a better look, and his great bone-headed mutt dived between us to see what we'd found, and cracked me a good one on the proboscis. Yes, there was a fair bit of claret and two black eyes, thank you for asking, but you can hardly see the bump now.

Lurchers are neat, agile dogs, and don't injure us all that often, not like some breeds I could mention. If you have a lurcher pelting towards you at warp ten and you stand still, it will almost always go around you rather than uproot you, though if you are lamping and it can't see you, don't take any chances. I've had rabbits run into my legs and it really hurts: I wouldn't like to try it with a lurcher. If you take someone lamping who has never been before, impress upon them that they must keep out of the way of dog and rabbit. Sometimes rabbits run up the beam straight towards the lamper, who should get out of the way sharpish while keeping the light on the rabbit and not dazzling the dog. I have known several people who thought they could trip the rabbit up as it dashed past by sticking out a leg. It's a damnfool thing to do because the dog is following far faster than they think: a fifty pound lurcher colliding with them at 30mph will hurt, but more importantly the impact may damage the dog seriously. Outside of lamping, several generations of my dogs would weave between the legs of people they liked, possibly as a way of getting stroked on both sides, and they would run through my legs and hide behind me if they were scared as well. As I am a short stumpy person with long lanky dogs, this can resemble extreme country dancing, especially if the ground is slippery.

Quite the best lurcher-related injury I ever saw occurred when I lived up a private lane that was a popular track for joggers. Some joggers get very fervent about their jogging, and ignore any crisis you might be having which is directly related to their thundering past. You can be clinging to a break-dancing horse, or trying to park in your own drive, which is only slightly larger than your car, but will they stop? Will they joggery. So when I returned from the vet with a litter of eight-

week-old Deerhound lurcher pups that had just had their MOT, and I yelled at the approaching joggist to stop while I unloaded them, I was not at all surprised when he ignored me and attempted to jog right through them instead.

He was wearing very short shorts and no jockstrap, which latter fact became apparent when the red-fawn puppy, always the comedian, jumped up and nipped a dangling thing (keen eyes, these sighthounds have). This instantly caused the rapid deceleration for which I had asked, plus a loud shrill noise which excited the other puppies. Next thing he was sprawled in the dust being jumped all over, licked, and nibbled with those very sharp spiky little baby teeth, but he wouldn't keep still and he would keep making a noise, so it was rather difficult for me to unpick seven baby lurchers from his sweaty person and push them through the back gate, especially as they thought this was the best fun they'd ever had. As fast as I fed them through the gate, out they would dash to play some more with their new squeaky toy. It wasn't long before the noises became harsher, now and then resembling words, until he realised he could actually get up, so up he got and off he went. I never even saw him leave because by then I was sitting on the ground too, howling with mirth and covered in puppies, which made for another lurcher-related injury because laughing so hard for so long really did hurt.

Twenty-one

The Deer Hunters

IN my glory days, I had a job which included inspecting the safety areas of seven airports - four in Scotland and three in the south-east of England. It was marvellous for a country girl because an airport's hinterland is a wildlife haven, and there was always plenty to watch and enjoy from the bee orchids at one site to hares boxing at another, the latter getting me out of bed very early so that I could see them at their best. Under the roar of the jet engines, wildlife of many kinds lived and thrived, largely undisturbed by people and clearly never having read anything about the alleged pollution that anti-airport protesters were very keen to blame for everything from global warming to oak trees dying. Airports have all sorts of legislation to meet, including that of being as environmentally friendly as possible, and the animals, birds, fish and plants that thrived in the outlying areas certainly seemed to appreciate our efforts.

My three colleagues, all city men, did not share my pleasure at seeing all this wonderful wildlife, and found any sudden appearance of mobile life forms rather disconcerting. I'll be the first to admit that a cackling cock pheasant straight up your shirt when you had your mind on inspecting runway approach lighting can be rather distracting, but even so I

felt that they were missing a lot by not taking an interest in being in the midst of such a treasure house. After a while, I stopped pointing out the rabbits, hares, foxes, birds and deer, but it was still a pleasure to see them; thank goodness only I seemed to notice the lizards and snakes. Within the

restrictions of the perimeter fence, however, wildlife becomes a hazard, from rabbits nibbling through essential electrical cables or undermining taxiways to birds with a death wish wanting to be sucked into aero engines, which last causes a sudden spraying of turbine blades over a wide area followed by a lot of noise and activity. Here too there are various legal obligations to be upheld, but outside the fence it was mostly a different matter, and the habitat was largely undisturbed apart from routine maintenance and inspection work.

One particular time we were in Scotland at the start of a four-day inspection when we found a certain amount of excitement taking place outside on the roads because a group of young stags had escaped from their deer farm (why would you want a deer farm in Scotland? It's lifting with them already) and were running riot. While we trudged across fields checking lights, we were periodically made aware of a Keystone Kops-style chase hurtling along the roads, involving a stag, one vehicle containing a driver and a passenger armed with a dart

gun, another vehicle carrying two people, and, bizarrely, a man on a bicycle who looked as if he was carrying a dart gun across the handlebars as well. As we were extremely busy and it was none of our business anyway, we didn't take a lot of notice.

Then, when we had come to the end of our detail that morning, and returned to the waiting staff Landrover to go back for lunch, we were suddenly in a prime position to see one of the stags walking towards us. The deer farm that was 'home' to him was up a track on our right, and the two vehicles plus the man on a bicycle were behind him, driving him slowly forwards. At some time he would have to come under sufficient pressure to turn down the homeward track, and it was clear from his general attitude that he had no intention of going back there.

Like most of you reading this, I have a healthy respect for large animals, especially a large one that was not precisely domesticated, and was wearing a Christmas tree on his head. But I am not afraid of them, and could see that some help was needed here. There was no way the somewhat frazzled team behind the stag was going to be able to turn it, but I and my colleagues were ideally placed. So I arranged all five foot four of me (and eight and a half stone in those days) just back of the turning, and spread my arms wide. The stag stopped. With four of us arranged across the track, the other three of whom were all much taller, and one who was wider as well, there was every chance of being able to turn the beast without him getting uppity. I hoped none of the lads would shout or move too fast and spook the deer. I fixed my stare onto him with that intent we in the know use when moving large potentially dangerous farm animals, concentrating all my energy on controlling him with my mind. He knew I was not afraid of him and I knew he was not afraid of me, so I did not dare to let my gaze falter. I took one slow step back and the stag took one step forward. Brilliant. He was almost abeam the turning, so I repeated the movement again and he stepped forward one more pace. I turned ever so slightly to the right to funnel him onto the track, and he dropped his antlers and charged.

I skipped aside; he brushed past me and set off for the town at a gallop, pursued once more by the weary crowd in the vehicles and yes, the man on the bicycle. I was so disappointed because we had come so near to achieving victory. Well, I had anyway. When I turned to speak to my colleagues I discovered why the deer had been bold enough to charge.

Far from being arranged beside me, every man jack of 'em was tucked safely away in the Landrover!

Twenty-two

Silence in the Field

YOU couldn't meet a nicer chap than Tom, but he's the noisiest beggar on Earth. It is unintentional and wholly natural: he could win awards for it. He likes to come out with the lurchers, and is on the receiving end of more lectures about keeping quiet than you would ever believe, but it doesn't seem to work. Take last Sunday.

Tom is a gem in the preliminary stages of ferreting. He'll clear any amount of brash in no time flat, chase roe deer off the land, net up the worst places and never complain, no, not even when the bank gives way and he falls into eighteen inches of icy water. Our little ferreting team works well together, and we let Tom make all the noise he wants, including several calls on his mobile, because we will then let the bury rest while we find some others to net. Then tea and a snack, The Lecture About Quiet, and back we go to the first bury, which is the serious one that we want to show the landowner results from. Buck takes out his mobile and ostentatiously switches it off. This is a Hint.

And this is Tom. He chats to the ferrets as he picks them up and lifts the nets for them. He walks like a centipede in galoshes, straight over the bury despite our frantic hand signals indicating that he should go round the side. He belches, gets glared at, and apologetically has an attack of hiccups. We

Photo: Fay Sechiari.

consider frightening him to cure them, but luckily they stop before we have worked out how to, and whether he might scream. He sniffs repeatedly until I hand him a tissue and then he stands right there on top of the bury and trumpets his nose into it. Actually, I'm not entirely sure that the last noise was his nose. When, despite this, the rabbits start bolting, he'll give us a commentary on what is happening his side of the hedge until someone can get there and glare at him again.

This particular day, the land had never been ferreted, the rabbits would have bolted with a brass band playing outside, and we were moving and shaking. We were on an old rubbish tip, and the ground gave way periodically, accounting for even more moving and shaking, but it had to be Tom who hit his head loudly on something, crashed through two broken pallets, well they were broken after that, and smacked down through a small elder tree, shivering his timbers to the extent that I didn't have the heart to glare at him. Then his mobile

110

went off and we all glared at him including the lurcher. He tried to explain that it must have switched itself on in his pocket, while I started giggling uncontrollably which started Buck off as well. Oh we do 'ave a laff. My lurcher, however, takes her work very seriously, and stalked off to monitor a rabbit hole as far away from this group of imbeciles as she could get. The rabbit she caught out of that was a very loud one and shrieked like a train-whistle; you could see the poor dog was getting a headache.

Picking up nets, digging a hole for the paunch and gutting out the rabbits seemed to take no time with Tom's running commentary, his obvious enjoyment of the day, and his

willingness to get his hands dirty or stung in tackling jobs he would never have dreamed of a few months ago. You could not meet a better lad. One day we're going to be very brave and take him lamping.

Twenty-three

Par for the Course

GOLF and lurchers are not all that compatible, but golf tends to occur on golf courses, which are very compatible indeed with a variety of wildlife. This in turn tends to attract lurchers, for their owners become all unnecessary when they see those hordes of rabbits skipping about on the green. Greenkeepers by contrast are reluctant to give permission on golf courses, and those of us who have managed to work our dogs in such places discover that there may well be a subspecies of super-rabbit that has evolved to live on the greens. These rabbits are fit, sleek, exceptionally fast, and can make fools out of very good dogs.

Their lifespan is enhanced by obstacles such as hidden bunkers, small spikes that stick out of the ground, and tarpaulin in unexpected places, often with hard things underneath. Add darkness and it soon becomes evident that golf courses are high-risk both for dogs and owners. In daylight, they tend to be in use by golfers, and so even if the greenkeeper is a friendly cove, opportunities for proper work are limited. Should your ferret lie up, there is no way you are going to be popular if you dig.

As a sapling, JB the fawn bitch was a cross-grained brat. I have had generations of her descendants and none that ever put me through it the way she did, due in part to all she taught me first. One day she swam the river and fetched up on the golf course the other side, where she made merry for some considerable time. A golfer gave her a sandwich (despite my shouted suggestion that he should do something else) and that was it. She did eventually swim back and I wasn't all that late for work, but she retained a fascination for golf courses that lasted all her life. While staying in Scotland, we were allowed to ferret a golf course, and the same dog helped a golfer find his lost ball, which may have explained his tolerance and forbearance shortly afterwards when she scorched after a rabbit and spoiled his swing by running between him and the tee. She did it again bringing in the retrieve. I found a nice net, though, and I still have it more than thirty years later.

Her son, the Bedlington Thing, chased a fox onto another golf course and tried to drag it out of a hollow tree while I shielded the action by standing in front, and prayed nobody

would hit a ball our way. His daughter became adept at golf course rabbits in the early mornings, for there was a footpath across a different one that passed invitingly close to some rabbity rough. Once I came across a forlorn young lad there, whose bull terrier was having a whale of a time in a bramble thicket, noises of crashing and smashing alternating with unmistakable Staffordshire heavy breathing and wheezing. You have to hand it to Staffordshire bullies: they are amazing at working heavy cover. She sent quite a few rabbits our way before she connected with the fox she'd been after. She retrieved it, too.

Fortunately I was never put in the position of serious embarrassment, unlike a friend whose dog put up a roebuck in broad daylight, which then headed for the fairway and sped across almost the full length of the immaculate sward. It fell over in front of a fairly appreciative crowd of Japanese businessmen, and mercifully the dog had plenty of experience, for the end was swift and neat. The dog's owner swung the buck across his shoulders, nodded at the audience and said, "Council. Been after this one for weeks", before bearing it away.

Twenty-four

Beating Dogs

*(Not an expose of canine abuse, but
an educational look at the use of dogs
in the beating line on a driven shoot)*

by Phillip Blackman

WHY do people have spaniels? In moments of weakness I've even considered having one but in the cold light of morning, with the headache comes a bit more common sense, and the realisation that only a simpleton would ever give house room to one of these stupid mutts. I mean, have you ever watched one of these brain dead curs work? Rushing around, tail going in all directions, those stupid ears flapping about like a head-shot pigeon's wings, and smashing through every bit of cover regardless of whether there's anything in it or not. Most of them appear to be deaf as well.

OK, I'm willing to acknowledge that in the hands of an expert (whatever that means) trainer who has rammed half a bottle of Valium down the damned thing's throat, a spaniel might be capable of appearing almost useful, but for the everyday shooter or beater such as myself who, being of a sensitive nature, gets fed up with shouting after a few hours, they're about as much use as a politician. "All right, Loudmouth", I hear you cry, "what dog do you recommend for beating?"

Well, a terrier, of course, I reply. Terriers are such sensible dogs. Okay, so some of them may have a penchant for potholing, but why shouldn't they have a hobby? Most, well some, of the time they'll be above ground and if the cover's thick and the birds are sitting tight they'll be quite happy to save the guns the price of a cartridge. Of course, in their enthusiasm they might not be quite as soft mouthed as a good spaniel, but then where would you find a good spaniel? On the shoot where I beat, one day when the team of guns weren't too good at their job, Winnie, my Patterdale/Border cross had contributed 10% of the bag at the end of the day on her own. The guns certainly saw enough birds to have shot the 300 they'd paid for but they seemed more than pleased with the 120 on the gamecart when they'd finished.

Terriers, you see, have too much common sense to rush around like loonies, flattening cover that holds no quarry. You watch them in the beating line. They'll toddle along picking their way delicately through the wood until their olfactory radar locks on to a target. Carefully they'll enter cover, creeping through thorns and bramble, under woodpile and hedge, until with the clichéd clatter of wings a pheasant erupts into the air, or doesn't. Should it be the latter the dog's handler will approach said dog and with a gentle throttling action accept the retrieve, possibly praising his hard working tyke with such words as "Leave the #@&*ing thing alone, you little bastard" or "For #@&~'s sake, that was my thumb, you evil little sod!" A few simple words of praise such as these will go a long way towards strengthening that bond between man and dog that is so important for a good working relationship.

Having retrieved the bits of pheasant, some handlers consider it useful to hold them as high as possible above their head and do a little dance whilst chanting "Leave it alone, you bastard. It's dead. Ow, that was my bloody leg!" Others surreptitiously hand them to a passing Labrador to take back to its owner.

Often, if the drive is fairly thick, one may not see much of one's dog, but the occasional flush of birds some way in front

and the polite request of the keeper to 'hold the line' may betray its whereabouts.

A hare, rabbit, fox, cat, wild boar, ostrich, pixie or goblin in the drive will tend to concentrate all the dogs' attention. Some may give tongue. Having pursued said hare, rabbit etc. through the drive and possibly a few others as well, some dogs may return.

On some drives, towards the end there could well be a concentration of birds between the advancing beaters and the flushing point. The desired objective in such a situation is for the birds to fly singly over the guns, thus providing the most shooting and allowing the guns time to reload, rather than for all the birds to flush at once. Faced with such a large flock of pheasants some dogs appear intimidated and are reluctant to approach them. Others are not.

One must not lose sight of why we and our dogs are beating. It is, of course, to have some sport, and if a shoot is not willing to provide its beaters with a healthy rabbit population, then there is something wrong. Therefore it is useful to have the odd lurcher or two in the team, especially on the more open ground. Many Labradors consider themselves to be lurchers, and some can become quite adept at snatching a passing rabbit but, if not lacking enthusiasm, they do lack speed in a chase. Spaniels may accidentally move rabbits whilst thrashing around, but are seldom aware of having done so.

Having looked at what is required of a dog for beating, let's now look at the dogs that regularly go beating on a shoot taken at random … Well would you believe it? The name of the shoot pulled out of the hat is the very shoot I beat for. Well I never, blow me down, goodness gracious, what a coincidence.

Still, that makes my life easier, as I don't have to travel to some distant shoot or interview anyone, and knowing all the dogs on our shoot, I can be relied upon to be totally unbiased.

So, with no further ado we'll start at the top. Mr Clutch, the shoot owner's Labrador, Fatty. Often Mr C will come to join us beaters to help out, and perhaps make useful suggestions, or as Don the keeper puts it "stick his bloody nose in". Fatty, as her name suggests, is a Labrador with too much access to Mr

C's grandchildren. The only time she is capable of moving at speed is if she falls over at the top of the hill. Being an almost perfect sphere she rolls well and a direct hit from a rolling Fatty could write off a Landrover.

Gabby, Don's wife, brings out one or more of her pack of terriers, or her springer, Peg. For a spaniel, Peg seems quite sensible, possibly due to frequent application of Gabby's holly stick. She has to be careful about bringing out her Jack Russells, as too long a dig can cause the guns to become impatient. Max, her Lakeland, isn't too much trouble as, like most of his breed, he appears to be under the influence of some form of proscribed substance.

Don the keeper may have with him any of the following: Billy, a large brindle lurcher, who really isn't interested in pheasants unless he's very hungry, but is always in the right place for a rabbit breaking cover from the bracken, and leads the pack in hare coursing. He's usually steady to deer but can be hard-mouthed with foxes. Sweep, a good-natured springer, who forgives Don for not understanding him. Polly, a black Labrador who was a gift from a trainer and who seems to be constantly practising for using a trampoline. Don no longer brings Ben, his aged terrier, whose face for some reason looks like he was distracted whilst juggling chainsaws, as the guns got a bit testy about his running up and down the line, screaming and pouncing upon and ragging any pheasant that was shot as soon as it hit the ground.

The Brigadier and Mrs Brigadier, whilst strictly speaking pickers-up and not beaters, may, if spoken to nicely, deign to help blank in. Their pride of Chesapeakes is not at all class-conscious and will bite anyone: gun, beater, dog, tractor, tree ... need I continue?

Puff and Dwayne, two very nice chaps, bring their vast pack of dung-brown dogs (chocolate Labs). Mother and daughters trained by Puff, they are the most obedient non-terrier dogs on the shoot. The mother does whine a bit, but then so does Dwayne, and Puff doesn't poke him with his stick.

Dick Barton has Heinz-Heel, a GSP who like all of his kind probably is aware of his master's existence but considers it bad form to acknowledge it. Dick doesn't help. He is a gadget man, and every day sees him with a different whistle or patent dog call. He is also incapable of doing two things at once. If he is calling his dog he cannot beat nor even walk as well. Whilst he fumbles with his tape recording of a tin of Chum being opened, the beaters either side of him fill in the gap and carry on. Heinz-Heel is like a bloody rambler. He gets everywhere.

Carl, the police inspector, has an extremely large black Labrador whom he instructs to bite people. Fortunately his dog, like his son, ignores him.

Lax, the bearded, bespectacled firearms enthusiast, is accompanied by two Labrador bitches, both well-trained but with expensive tendencies towards barbed wire and postmen's legs.

Paul Dee has two spaniels, a giant springer named Geronimo and the prettiest little black cocker you've ever seen, called Jack. If I didn't know he was a spaniel I could really like Jack, but when he's working he's just as unintelligent as the rest of them.

Mick, Don's father's English springer spaniel is even more vicious than a Chesapeake. Because the damned thing is so hideously deformed (I think his parents belonged to someone who worked at a nuclear reprocessing plant) his claws grow out of the top of his feet and require frequent clipping. This calls for Don's old man and Gabby to sit on him with a coat over his head whilst Don hacks the offending talons down to size. After this major surgery it is best if all participants run like buggery before he shakes the coat off. The old boy says he's a lovely dog and a real character even though the dog won't allow him on the furniture at home.

Jimmy the fireman used to bring his old Rottweiler bitch out. She was an extremely gentle creature. The only time she ever hurt anything was when she once accidentally trod on a cow. She always seemed to look upon beating as being quite a nice walk in the woods. He now brings Pat, his nondescript terrier who thinks he's a spaniel, or his new Staffordshire bull terrier who for some reason is mainly kept on the lead. We like to play a little game called guess the tune as she can be somewhat vocal when excited. Lastly there is myself and the aforementioned Winnie. We are obviously well thought of by Don as we are always being sent off to blank in some distant wood on our own for a future drive, "just in case", as Don puts it "we need an extra drive at the end of the day". We never seem to, but all the same are very grateful for Don's confidence in giving us this very responsible job. Although Winnie and I may be on the far side of the shoot from where the action is and even out of hearing of the shooting most of the time we still have some fine sport and see quite a lot of the pack in full cry as they pass by.

Twenty-five

Cock Up

by Phillip Blackman

THE shoot on which on I beat is one of those famous high bird commercial shoots of which one hears so much these days. This is an account of the traditional beaters' day shoot.

Persona Dramatis. *(Names, as they say in the best of journalistic circles, have been changed to protect the innocent(?))*

American Ray the famous sleeping stop.

Ted the retired bobby and chief stop.

Puff and Dwayne with their countless, interchangeable pack of brown dogs (Chocolate Labs).

Carl the police inspector, father of Thomas, owner of Ken, a bullock-sized black Labrador, and possessor of a rapid and acerbic wit.

Jimmy the fireman with Pat the terrier and Rags the Rottweiler.

The Brigadier and Mrs Brigadier, small beef farmers with a stocking rate of just under two to the square yard, with their Chesapeake Bay retrievers: a dog slightly smaller than a tractor with a tendency to juggle spaniels, and two bitches with much nicer natures. Well, they haven't bitten anyone today anyway.

Four members of the **Murphy** family, local farmers, rumoured to own slightly more land than Paul McCartney and be slightly better off than the Sultan of Brunei despite turning up in a vehicle consisting of a collection of rust held together by holes. Most of them lame and/or very old.

Nat the dog trainer, smells of Labrador, cocks his leg on trees in passing, has been known to whine in presence of an attractive female and upon meeting same invariably gets his face slapped and then cocks his leg up the nearest tree. Beats spaniel.

Don the Keeper. Suffers from shell-shock, apoplexy and sore throat from shouting at beaters and spaniel all season. Keeps phone number of Samaritans in top pocket and has strange glazed look in eyes. With Sweep the spaniel and Billy the lurcher. Beats spaniel.

Gabby, wife of Don, pops Valium. Has Peg the spaniel with her. Beats spaniel.

Terry, the shoot owner. Addressed as Sir, Mr Clutch sir, God, or by his keeper at the end of a spectacularly unsuccessful, but damned hard work to do, drive, 'well that was a bloody good idea, wasn't it?'

Kevin, Terry's son, keen shot and all round good egg, with his yellow Labrador Bella.

The Frenchman, Terry's business associate guest who seldom misses and is 100% safe. So much for the stereotypes.

Frank. No one knows who he is, but he turns up every beaters' day.

Yours truly, lowly narrator. Brought Winnie the Patterdale/Border cross out for the day.

Once everyone is assembled, the day starts with the normal pre-shoot talk from Don. "No ground game. Standing guns shoot cocks and hens. Walking guns shoot cocks only going back. No ground game. Be safe. Enjoy yourselves." He splits us into two teams: A and B, which is easy to follow. Calls for team A to follow him. Everyone does. He jumps up and down, swears a bit and divides us once more into two teams A and B and tells us to remember which team we're in this time. Calls for team A to follow him. Everyone stands still. He jumps up and down a bit more. His voice is getting croaky and

the veins on his neck are standing out. He considers shooting team A in left foot and team B in right. Decides not to. Not on humanitarian grounds, but because we don't know our lefts from our rights. Physically pushes half of us to the left and half to the right and patiently and in words of one syllable explains which team we're in and that we are to remember this time or else we can all go home. Terry in his Landrover full of Frenchman and lame Murphies looks on and says nothing. I am in team A. First drive: The standing guns are the Frenchman, lame Murphies and team B. Team A are walking guns. American Ray is sent off to walk-in distant hedge on top of the hill. Initial complicated blanking-in procedure involves teams A and B blanking-in area the size of China. There is much shooting and shouting. Spaniel is beaten. We arrive as instructed in a fairly straight line on the correct woodland ride. No sign of Don. I send team B off to stand forward. Frank smiles and asks what's going on. I confess to having no bloody idea. A cock parts my hair, followed by a load of number sixes. Make mental note to keep away from Frank. Drive starts and am approached by delegation from team B, who ask what's going on. I think we're going this way. Point. Cock parts my rapidly thinning hair, followed by load of number sixes. Must avoid Frank. Has anyone seen Winnie? Team B wanders off in direction of point. Much shooting from all directions. Cock falls at my feet. Hide behind tree in case Frank's about. After half an hour crawl out. Dead cock jumps six feet in the air. Frank's been stalking it. Develop twitch. Reach end of first drive. Fall to knees to give thanks for surviving it.

Volunteer to go and feed for third drive on quad bike. Call Winnie. Wander off and hide gun in grain bin. Drive up and down drawing birds into third drive. Drive into tree. Kick quad bike. Hop up and down holding foot. Drive about a bit more until approached by suspicious-looking bunch armed with shotguns. About to start crying when recognise team A. Park quad bike and retrieve gun. Poke stick down barrels to get rid of grain. Stop to talk to American Ray. Learn he's shot two pheasants on the ground.

"Gee those crazy birds jumped up in the air." Leave him in middle of large field. "Sometimes a hare comes this way. I want to have a shot at him." I remember something my father used to say about the war.

I join the walking guns. Hear distant croaking sounds like crow saying "something bastard". Spaniel yelps. Fail to frighten passing pigeon. Call Winnie. End of drive. Brigadier informs Don that about twenty birds broke out of left-hand side. He pales visibly at the reply. A Labrador chunders up pheasant by Landrover. Fourth drive: Call Winnie. Jimmy's terrier does the drive on his own whilst Jimmy sensibly keeps quiet. Puff and Dwayne argue over which brown dog is which. Miss Woodcock. Fall over and slide down hill on arse. Arrive at feet of benevolent keeper who fires shot into ground at my feet, giggles and says in slurred fashion "Dance, stranger." Climb back up hill. Meet Ted the ancient stop with large pile of pheasants and big grin. Congratulate him and help carry them to the Landrover. Cock polishes my bald pate. I throw myself to the ground. "Its all right," says Ted, "Frank's down the bottom." A load of number sevens pass by. "American Ray's not." I reply, aware of an involuntary moistness.

Lunch: I call Winnie. Sarnies and a flask of tea comes out of my bag, from the Brigadier's a bottle of cherry brandy, Puff and Dwayne have some sloe gin and Jimmy a flask of whisky and ginger. When it has all gone, and the volume of conversation is greatly increased, someone suggests a visit to the off-licence and staying in the beaters' hut is a better idea than going out shooting again. We agree that if breathalysed on the way home we can give Carl the police inspector's name. He groans. His son, Thomas, asks Dwayne why he has an inflatable sheep. Carl groans again.

Assembling for the afternoon shift Jimmy has substituted Rags the Rottweiler for his terrier. I call Winnie. Checking my team is to stand for the first drive I put my stick away and get out the gun. We are all given a briefing for this drive by Don, in a hoarse whisper. Our neighbour, a strange lady, puts sheets out in her paddock to collect any fallen shot in order to whinge about it, so therefore do not shoot in the direction of the boundary is our instruction. I ask if anyone's seen Winnie. We all get into various vehicles. Rags and Jimmy get in the Range Rover. I'm in the middle seat of Don's Landrover. Every time he changes gear he touches my knee. Is this the start of a wonderful romance? I wonder where Winnie is. Both teams are to blank in together. Standing team at the bottom of the hill, walking at the top. I meet Terry with his black Labrador, Fatty. "Pretend I'm not here", he says "carry on". Kevin to my left frightens a woodcock. There is much shouting from the impenetrable mass of hawthorn above us. Hearing a spaniel yelp I'm reminded of Winnie. A brown dog sends a cock bird back over me. I miss. Looking round, Terry's disappeared. Reaching the valley in which we are to stand, Don places us, me at peg number four. Kevin is called down to back gun me on the valley floor, not on top of the bank behind me. Don talks with Kevin. He's only seen this drive from the beaters' side before and wants to see how they fly over the guns. Team

B, not realising team A have stopped, cock it up and only half a dozen or so birds instead of a couple of hundred fly over us. Kevin drops one, the Frenchman another. They're bloody miles up. This is ridiculous. How do they do it? The spaniel retrieves both. Don smiles. He's seen what they're like. The Brigadier says nothing.

Back to the car park, and we'll do the bit of wood we started at again. With a pause for the standing guns to get into position we, the walking guns, start off. Kevin and I have snuck off on our own to the left above the reservoir. Swinging through a cock bird put up by Kevin, my barrels get stuck in a sapling, and it carries on. I call Winnie. The standing guns out in the field aren't getting much shooting as most birds are going back over the car park. "Hold the left" croaks Don. Kevin sits down. A cock takes his hat off and swinging round he drops it. As the drive ends a bird comes towards me. Bang. The only hen of the day drops on Kevin. "No, it's the pretty ones, Phillip" he calls out.

Back at the car park once more, and young Thomas has shot a heap of pheasants going back and Winnie has retrieved her kill and it's not a fox.

Twenty-six

Dark Ridge

THERE'S a 'school's out' feeling to the last few weeks of ferreting, because our season is governed not by the date but by hormones, livestock and weeds. Ferrets come into breeding fettle and have other kinds of ferreting on their minds, rabbit kittens appear, dashing through the net mesh or staying underground and giving the ferrets the run-around, tiny new nettles are delivering a winter's worth of stored-up venom not just on bare skin but through our clothing too, and farmers are turning out livestock and wanting their fields back from our attentions. For others, the cut-off comes at the peak of their sport, when the calendar suddenly says "No More" and they are going home with dogs or hounds and horses fit as fleas and nothing to do next Saturday, but we ferreters, we are luckier, because we can wind down more gently.

This is when we bring out the 'B' team - the old ferrets or last year's kits, the novice dogs just starting or the senior ones that can't do a full day any more, and we tackle the small and tricky buries that use up too much time on a short winter day when we could be cracking on with the big ones. Unlike

Photo opposite: Fay Sechiari.

Photo: Fay Sechiari.

with most other fieldsports, we have the chance to work with a lighter attitude than during the serious stuff of the main season. Our landowners have seen results, and we can afford to give the odd rabbit a sporting chance for the benefit of educating a young dog or making an old one feel worthwhile, or to try something new and see if it works. Now is the time we can turn our attention to those rough and hungry places that only hold a handful of rabbits, those asbo types evicted from the main buries because of social undesirability. The huge buries that we tackle in the depths of winter, when rabbits are underground in quantity and we go mob-handed to clear them, will be left until after harvest now.

Rabbit dynamics change at this time too, for now is when they are found in pairs or fours rather than the big groups of winter rabbits. Set seven nets or seventy, there will only be one or two pairs in each bury, so the time taken netting has to be set against the likely result, which gives a time-management reason to leave the nets in the bag, or else only net a few holes, and let the dogs run instead.

So our final few weeks at the game have a certain levity about them: it is a mopping-up operation on the periphery of serious rabbit control. Now we can afford for a rabbit to escape here and there, to give a young lurcher its first taste of what happens when the ferret slides underground. If a 'squeaker'* bolts, the net won't hold it because it flits straight through the mesh, but it's an easy confidence-giving catch for an apprentice dog. Start them on small buries and small numbers of rabbits, just one or two ferrets down so the bolts come one at a time, and you lay foundations for a good fcrrcting dog, whereas a sensitive youngster might be overwhelmed by the fast action of big buries on a winter's day, or those long waits in sour weather when rabbits are reluctant to leave at all. A ferreting dog - as opposed to a dog that goes ferreting - has much to learn, and needs a quiet arena to learn it. Critical to the learning process is stopping before the dog gets bored, exhausted or too cold to enjoy itself, as well as ending on a good note rather than yielding to temptation and doing one more bury.

Our last full day as a team is always spent on Dark Ridge. Folded so deeply into the South Downs that the sun rarely penetrates, it is best reached by four-wheel drive, hang-glider, or setting out the day before. As we can usually only manage one 4WD, we shoehorn everything we need into it using a method called 'somehow', and with our younger members clinging to the sides and the dogs running behind, we chug as far up the ridge as we can before we have to take up our baggage and walk. There will be a certain amount of dismay occasioned by the fallow deer departing (three black does, one cream buck), and then the ground is ours. Dark Ridge buries are old and deep, and have been occupied for centuries, apart from a hiccup in the early years of myxomatosis. Rabbits are big and fat, for not much bothers them up here apart from foxes and buzzards. In summer, nettles tuft the warrens so that neither dog nor ferret is willing to investigate, while rabbits slide unscathed between the leaves. Even terriers baulk at Dark Ridge nettles. But now last year's nettles are mere brown stalks, with the new ones only just beginning, and we have a short time of access each year between the old nettles dying off and the new ones coming up. If only it wasn't such a pig of a place to get to, but the bigger the challenge, the more the fun.

We pick one bury per dog with plenty of space between because they are here to learn a job, not eye up other dogs, and whoever has the camera this time stalks from bury to bury seeking that career-making shot. As the day unfolds, a sun we can't feel glows half-heartedly above us, and a buzzard slides past sideways to see if we are paunching-out yet. Sorry old chap, but regulations say we must bury our paunch, even if the fox digs it up half an hour later. Maybe he'll leave you some. Our young ferrets gain in confidence with every try below ground: at first they are uncertain, hesitating at the rabbit holes, but before long they are fluffing-up and shaking out like falcons rousing, and then dashing underground. They aren't always so pleased to be picked up once they are really enjoying themselves. A spectacular burst of nautical English indicates that one ferret has become over-excited and nipped

the hand that feeds it, while on another bury, one of us is lying on the ground up to his armpit in rabbit-hole, with a ferret holding onto the other end of the rabbit he is gripping. This is when a helpful dog comes up and licks your face.

If you can possibly avoid digging at Dark Ridge, it is a good decision. Therefore when a ferret is slow to reappear, we use locators to see if it is moving or still, always supposing that it hasn't gone too deep for the locator to locate, but we delay that graft moment as long as we can. Tyro ferrets don't always have the courage to penetrate deeply into these old buries, and can sometimes be dislodged by putting an older ferret in, but it is a case of knowing your ferrets because it would be so easy to turn one problem into two. So there is time to sit and watch, and usually the issue resolves by itself. A little brown long-eared head might appear cautiously at this hole and then that, before committing to a bolt, or more usually a sneak-out between the dried-up nettle stems. This is where the novice dog might move too soon, but will learn by its mistake, where the canny old dog will stand motionless on three legs, one front foot raised and only the twitching ears showing what she knows. At exactly the right distance she will pounce and lift the rabbit, turning to look at you with eyes snapping triumph. And with luck, a few moments later, out will come your missing ferret, sniffing myopically along the scent of its quarry. "Did any of you get that?" it asks. "I worked my butt off to shift it."

Dark Ridge days end quite early, with the paunching-out ceremony into a hole someone could not avoid digging, and a shaman-like inspection of the entrails for such interesting matters as pregnancies and parasites. Anything unusual such as tooth deformity or injuries is photographed unless batteries have gone flat, and then we realise, as we do every year, that we have to carry everything, including our pile of rabbits, up to the top of the Ridge, where the vehicle awaits. Hocked rabbits are slung along graft and slasher handles, as well as lengths of rope brought in the net bags for the purpose, and we slog our way to the top. Once there, the view is awesome, and we stop for a long survey while our breathing eases and the tadpoles cease to shimmer before our eyes. As a concession to geriatrica, I only have to get myself up the Ridge while the young 'uns carry the gear, but even so my breathing is the harshest, and hypoxia beckons. Then there is the tea ceremony, when flasks are shared and the contents of lunch bags pooled, where food has never tasted so good despite the lingering pong of rabbit guts, and the dogs lie close, waiting for crusts, except for the one looking longingly at the fallow,

which are just creeping back over the rise. A sharp word, and the dog sinks apologetically back down again, flattening its ears in supplication, when all is forgiven and it gets a piece of pork pie.

We might, as individuals, have the odd nip-and-tuck few hours here and there after the Dark Ridge day, but that is the official end of our ferreting season, and it can come at any time between March and the end of April. We will still be hunting rabbits through the summer, but by different ways. Ferrets will be breeding, maybe there will be a litter of puppies in our circle, the old dogs will have a lazy summer and the young ones will learn some new skills. There are nets to check and mend, and bags, ferret boxes, collars and locators to refurbish or replace. We shoehorn the gear plus pile of rabbits into the vehicle, and walk back behind it, downhill all the way, feeling the cold and that contented tiredness that you only get from a long day out of doors at your chosen sport.

*rabbit kitten